A BEGINNER'S BOOK FOR MANUSCRIPT WRITING

"GOD MADE MY WORLD"

This book belongs to:

By Carol Ann Retzer

A Concerned Communications Publication

author: Carol Ann Retzer
senior editor: Bill Morelan
copy editor: Patricia Horning Benton
cover design: Daniel Potter
cover illustration: Mary Bausman
inside illustration and design: Walt Woesner

For more information about A REASON FOR WRITING®, write or call:
Concerned Communications
P.O. Box 1000
Siloam Springs, Arkansas 72761
Telephone (501) 549-9000

 Printed on recycled paper

Let's Start at the Beginning

In the beginning God made our world—your world. In this book you will find many pictures of animals, plants, and other things that God created. You will do a special project with each picture!

These pictures and activities will help you remember the letters of the alphabet that they stand for. You'll discover that learning about God's world is a lot of fun!

You're at a new beginning, too. In this book you'll explore the beginning of written letters. You may have drawn pictures and copied words already. But this book will take you letter-by-letter through the whole alphabet.

A tree house is an exciting place to explore! You'll get to know a very special tree house in this

ROOF

ATTIC

MEETING ROOM

LADDER

book. There's a right way to make each letter. The tree house will help you remember where each letter goes on the handwriting line.

When we start anything, we want to do it the right way. Holding your pencil is one thing that will help you write your best. Look at the picture to help you know the correct way. It's also good to sit up straight in your chair and slightly slant your book or paper the same way as your arm.

We're off to enjoy a year in God's world! Have fun—and do your best every day.

Correct Formation of Letters

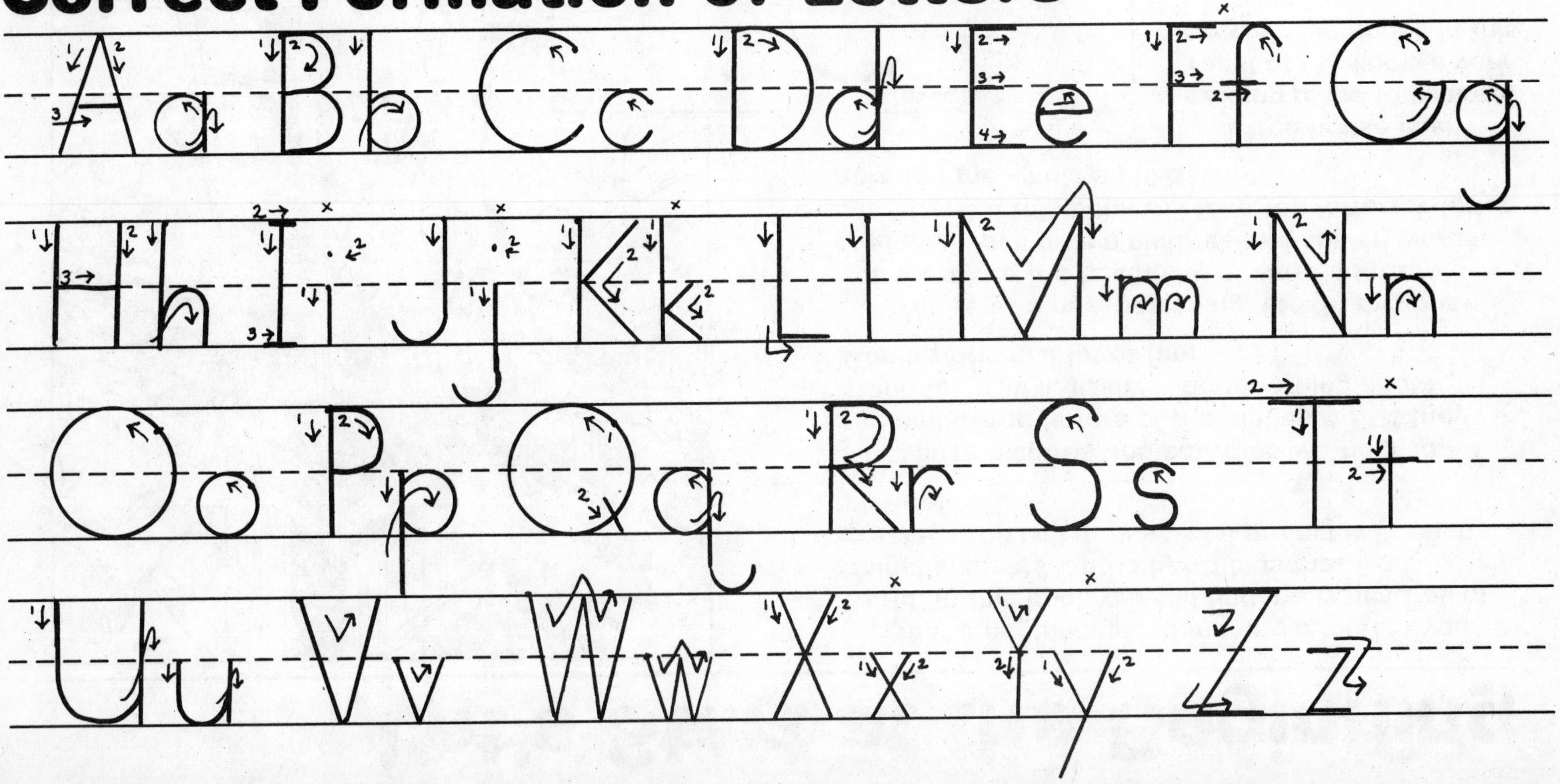

Give to the Parent or Guardian

Dear Kindergarten Parent or Guardian,

As your child begins this school year, you are an important part of the education process. We want to tell you about the handwriting lessons your child will be completing.

Each letter lesson is based on God's creation - learning more about the amazing facts of nature as we learn to write.

We want to give each student the skills to make writing an exciting and easy process. It is amazing how much easier writing can be (both printing and cursive writing) when letters are formed correctly.

Letter formation is so important. Generally, letters are made circle to the left and stroke down on straight stroke letters. Top to bottom (not bottom to top) letter formation will make the transition to cursive so much easier and natural. Most lower case letters are formed

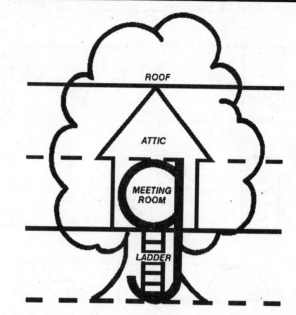

without picking up the pencil. (The letters that are formed with two strokes are marked with an x.)

There are directional arrows on most pages as well as on the model alphabet on the back of this letter.

In class we will talk about a tree house, with letters made in the meeting room, or going down to the ground, as in letter g.

Handwriting is indeed a life skill. While some may

think of printing as only a beginning point, we view it as something that is important throughout life. Think of the number of times you are asked to print on an application or other document.

How can you help? Enjoy seeing the pages your child brings home. Let him/her show you how they wrote the letters. Be positive as you see progress.

Continued . . .

Encourage correct formation in writing letters on the line and filling the space. This will take time and practice.

Because we all learn in different ways, the students may be describing the letters, writing letters in the air, feeling letters by writing in sand or fingerpaints. These are things you can do with your child as well. You can write any letter with your index finger on the palm of their hand, or let them write it on your palm. You can "write" the letter on their back and let them guess the letter. All this helps them picture each letter. This is important in the process of eventually writing each letter without thinking how it is made.

Wishing you a wonderful year writing and enjoying God's world,

Carol Ann Retzer
Author

Correct Formation of Letters

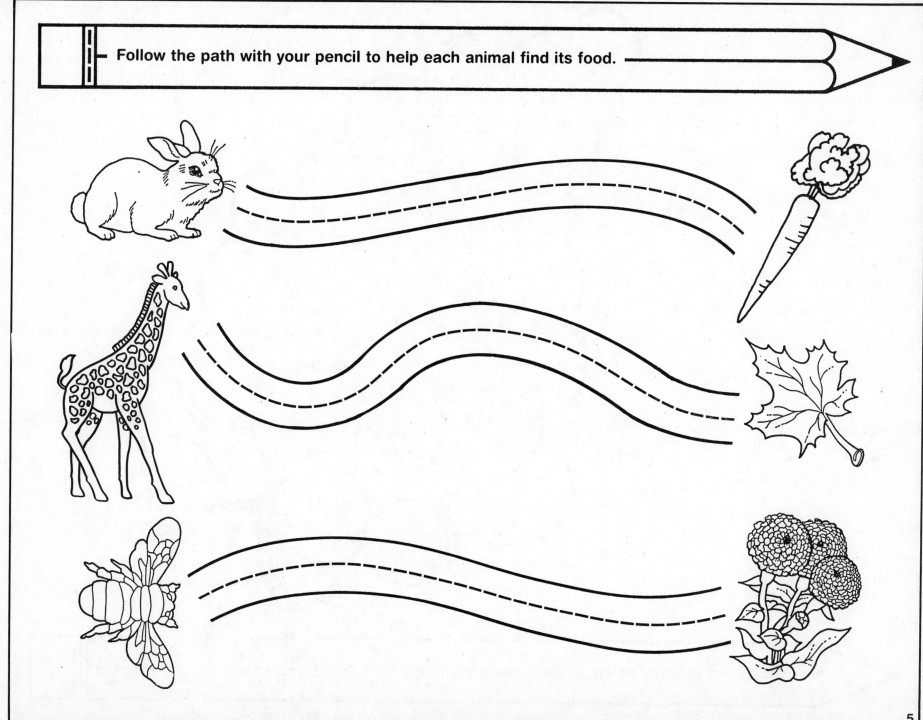

Follow the path with your pencil to help each animal find its food.

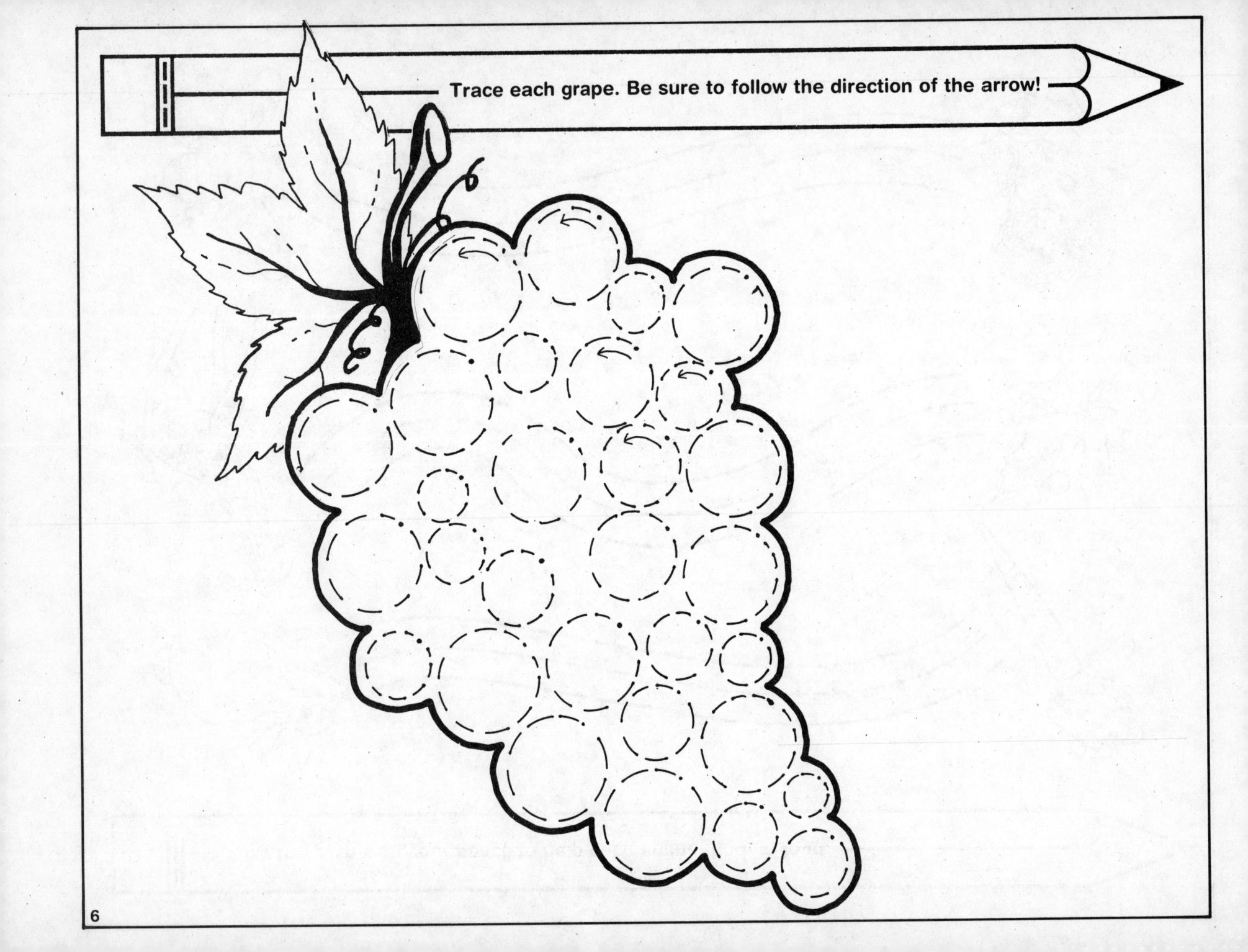

Trace each grape. Be sure to follow the direction of the arrow!

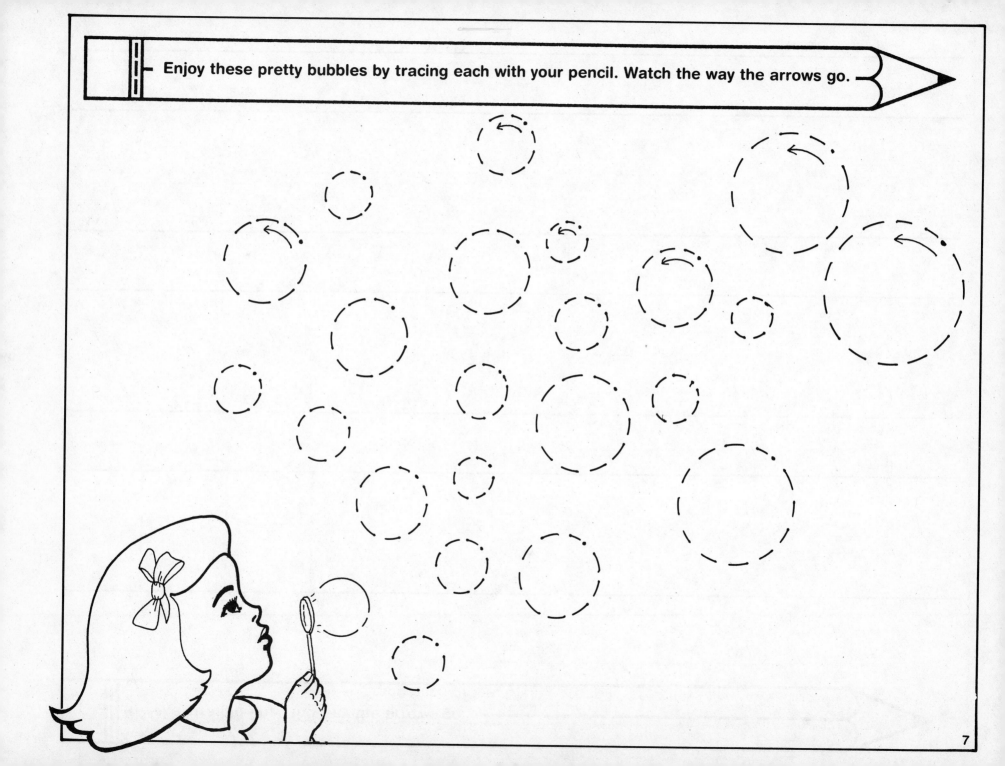

Enjoy these pretty bubbles by tracing each with your pencil. Watch the way the arrows go.

7

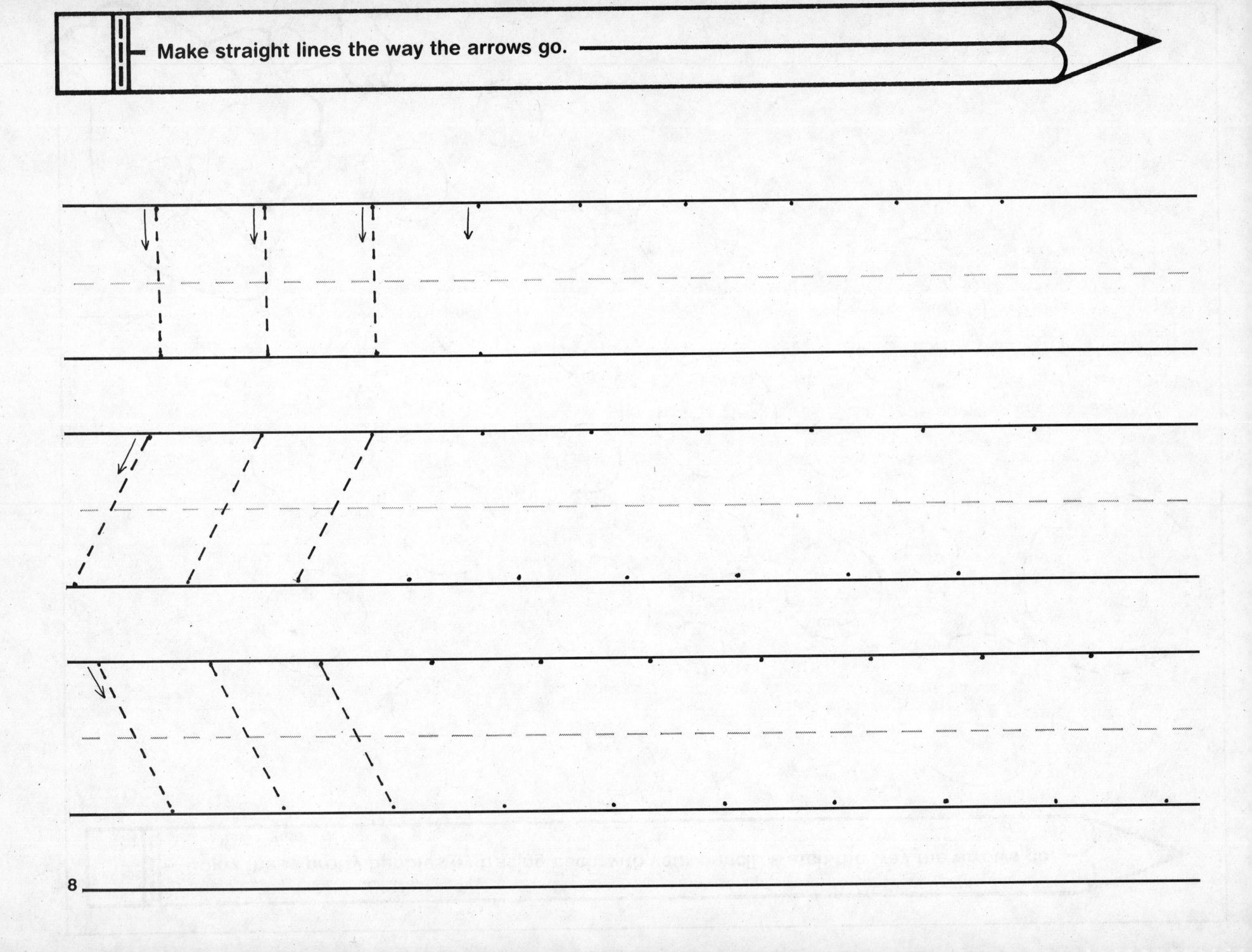

Make straight lines the way the arrows go.

8

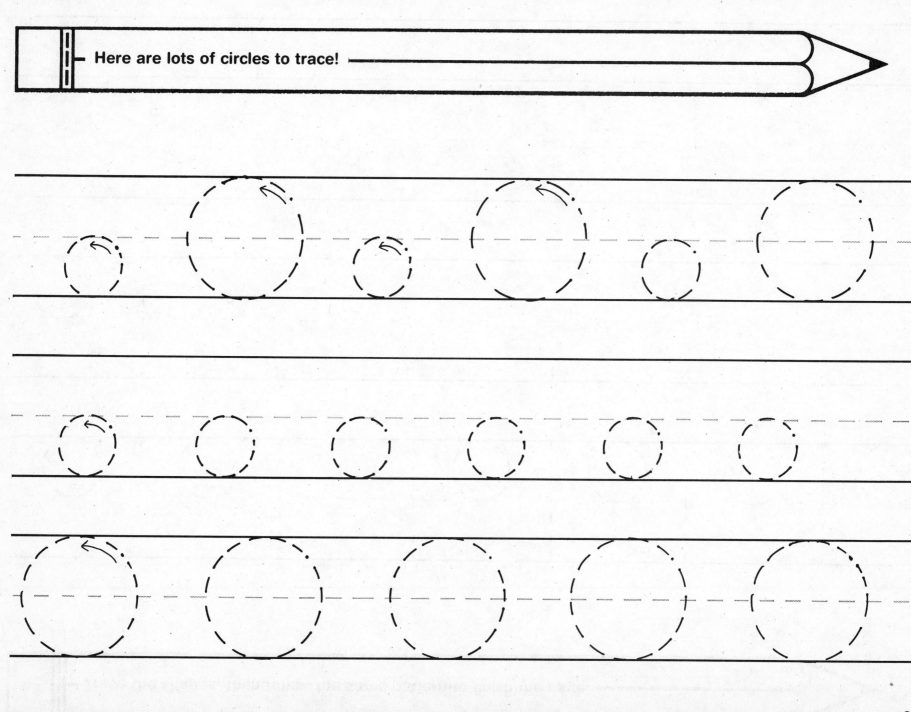

Here are lots of circles to trace!

10

11

Don't fish make nice bubbles? Trace every one.

12

octopus

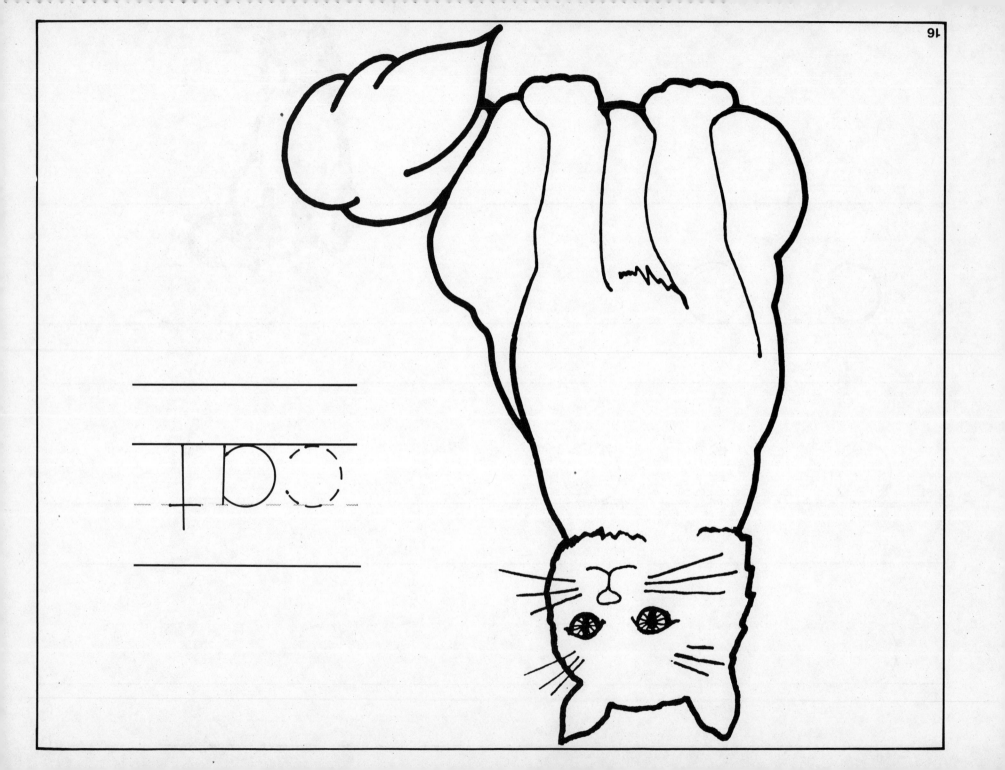

cat

goose

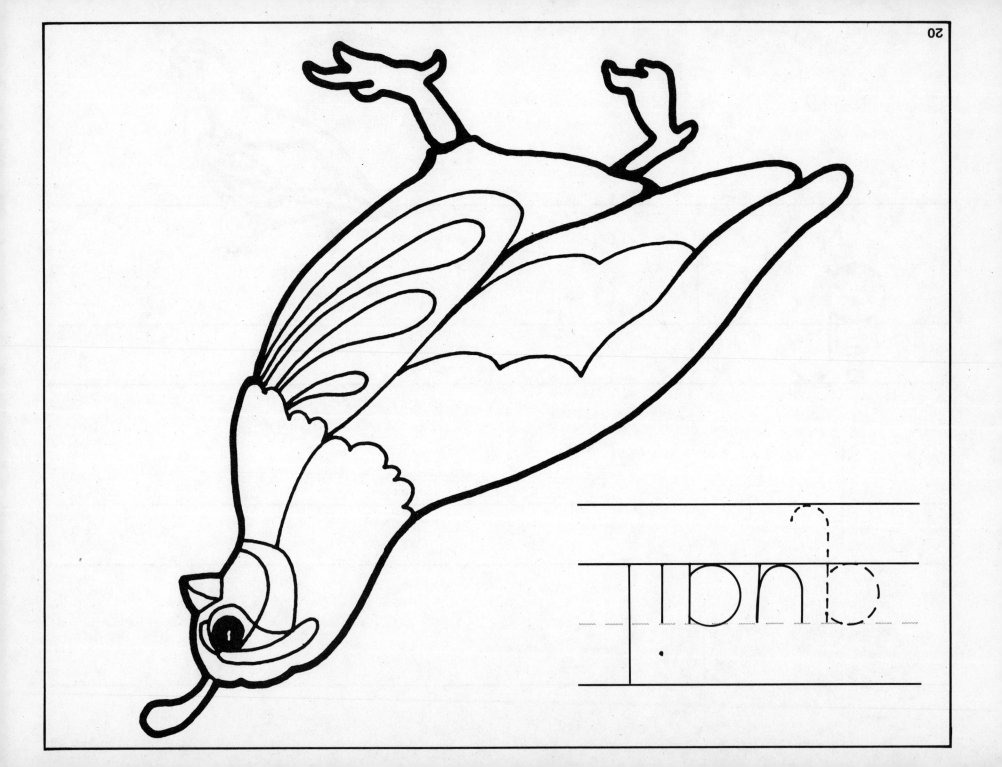

quail

Libus

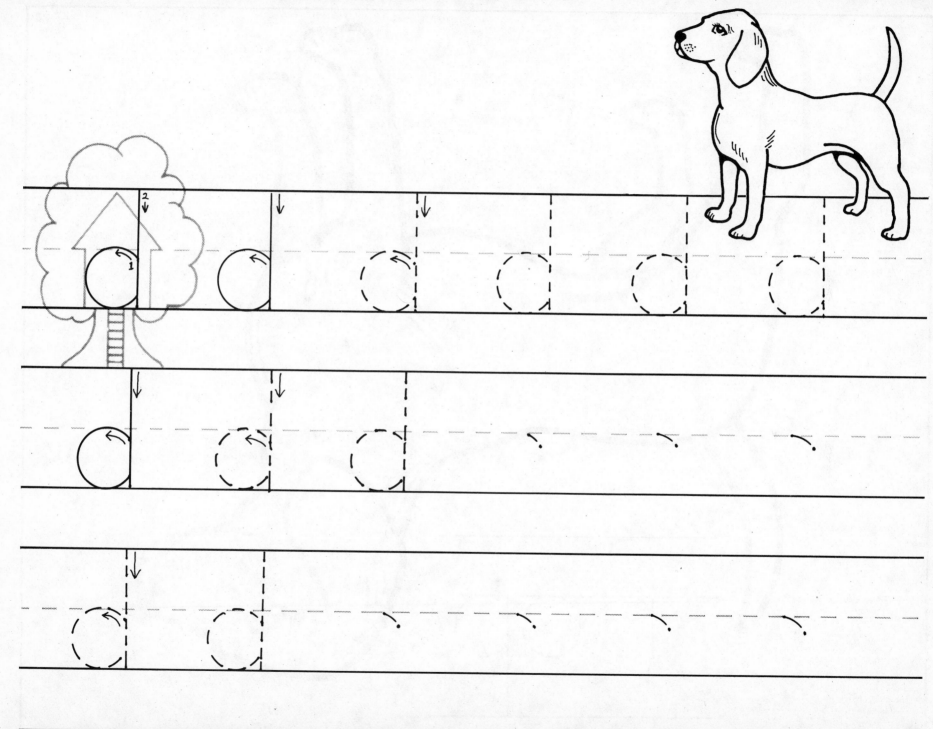

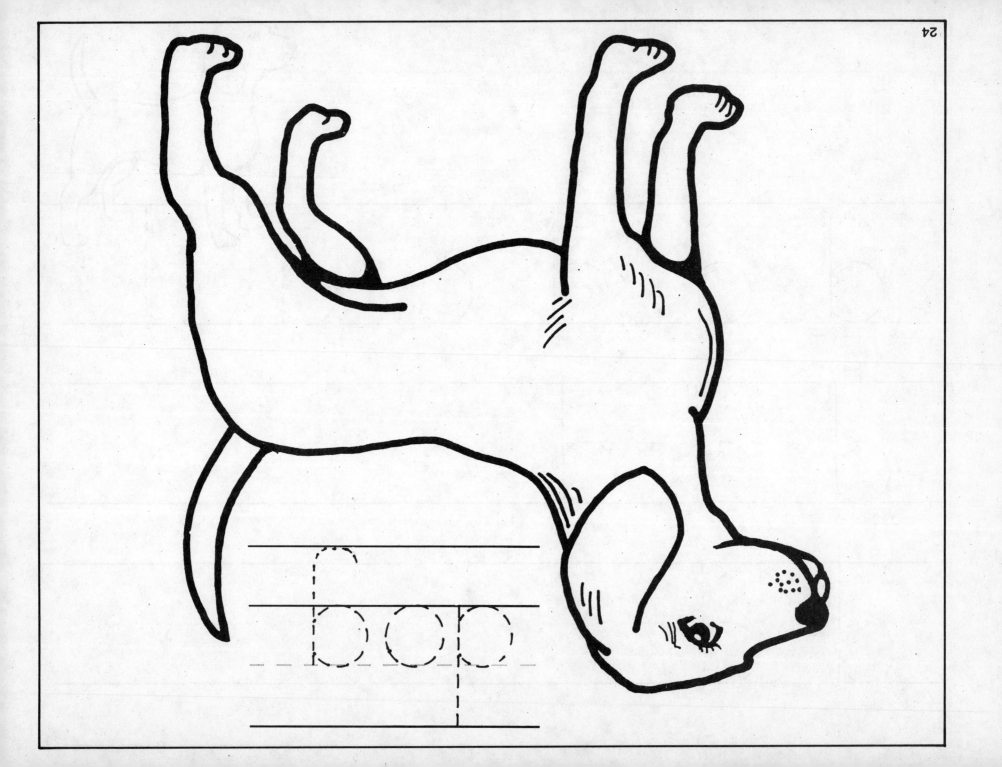

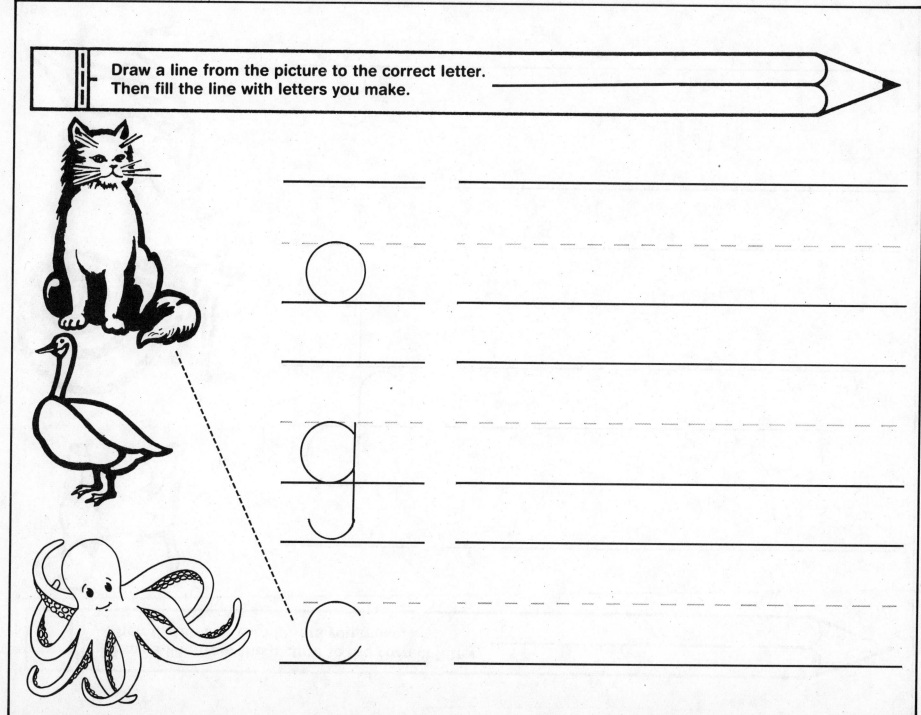

Draw a line from the picture to the correct letter.
Then fill the line with letters you make.

25

Draw a line from the picture to the correct letter.
Then fill the line with letters you make.

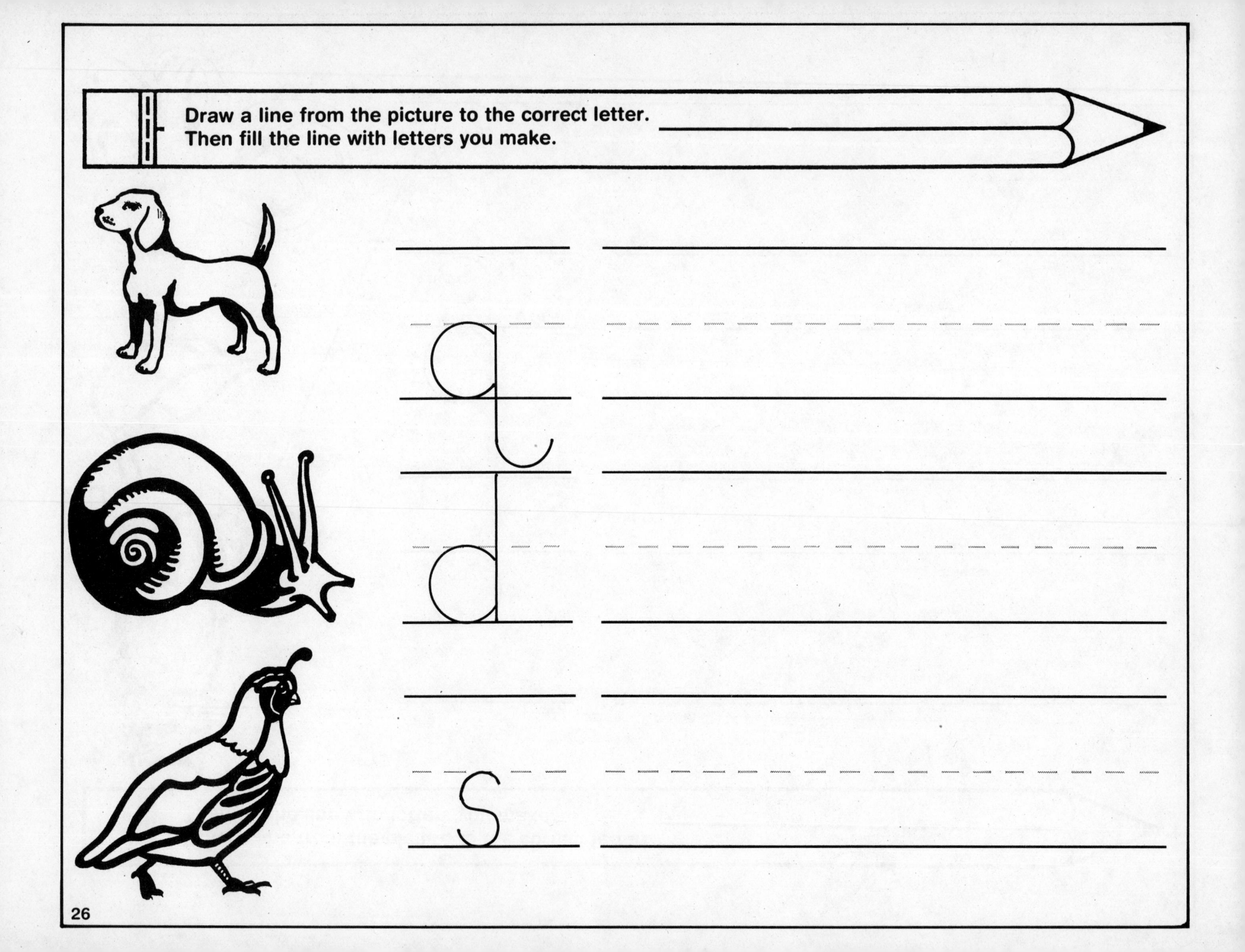

d

a

s

apple

bear

pumpkin

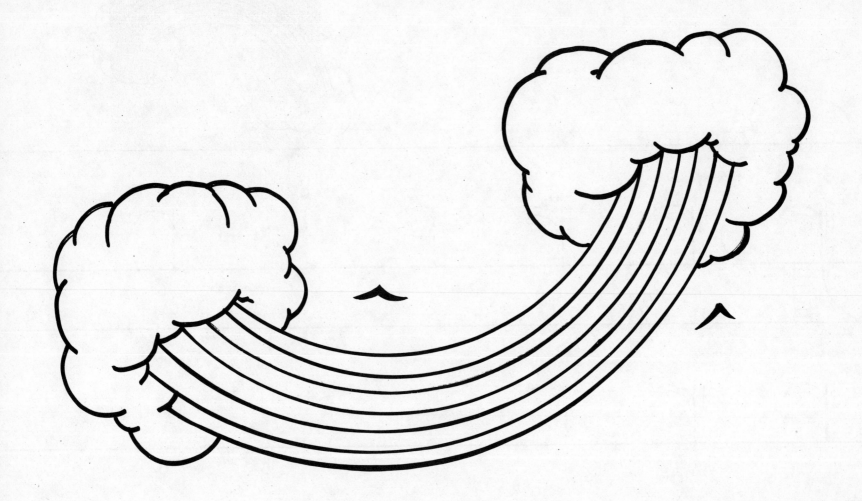

rainbow

u o o u

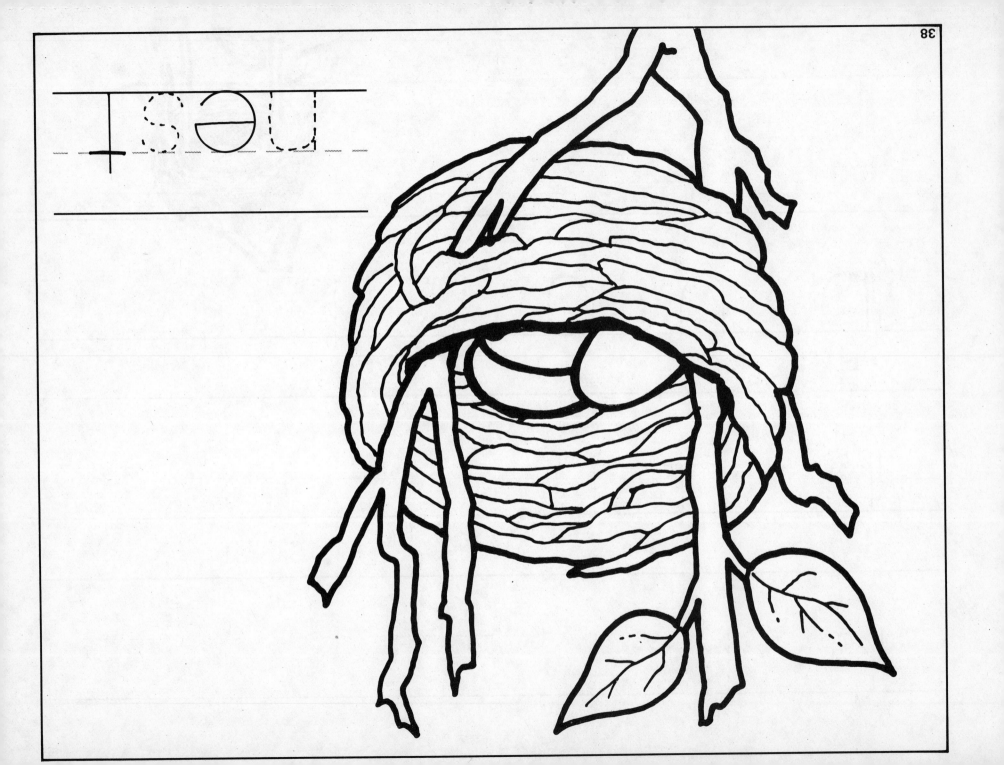

Draw a line from the picture to the correct letter.
Then fill the line with letters you make.

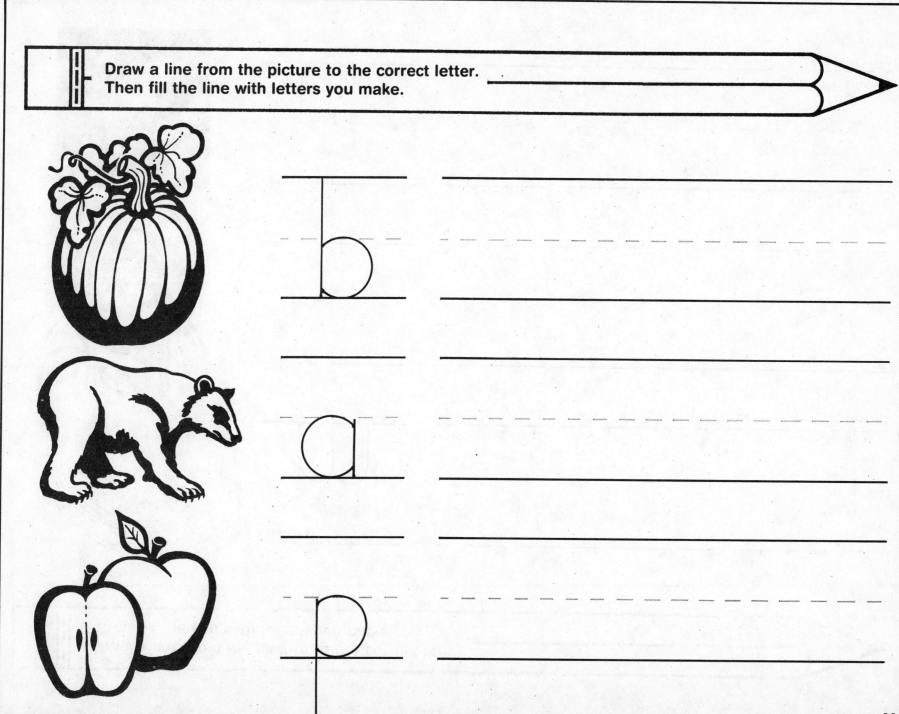

b

a

p

Draw a line from the picture to the correct letter.
Then fill the line with letters you make.

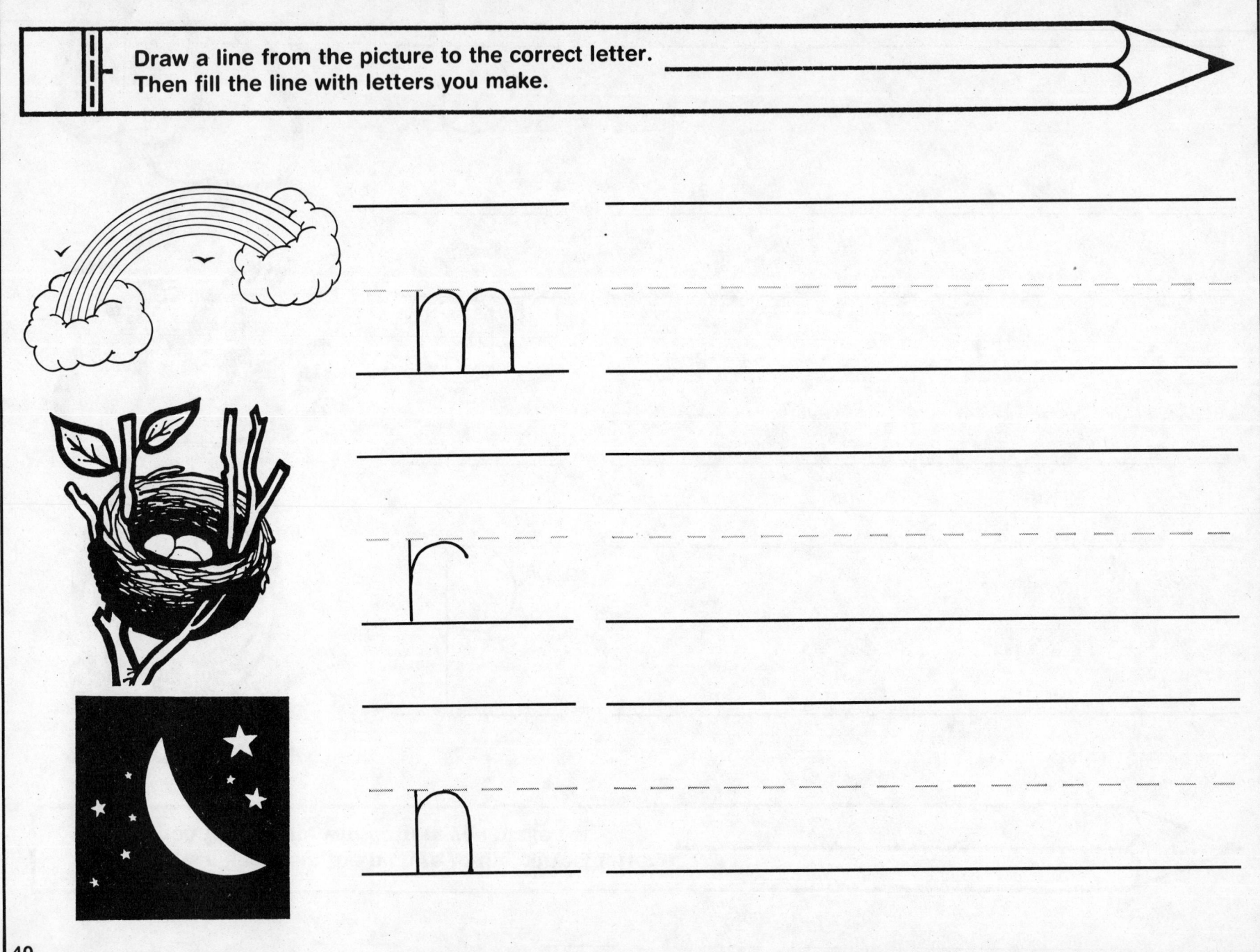

m

r

n

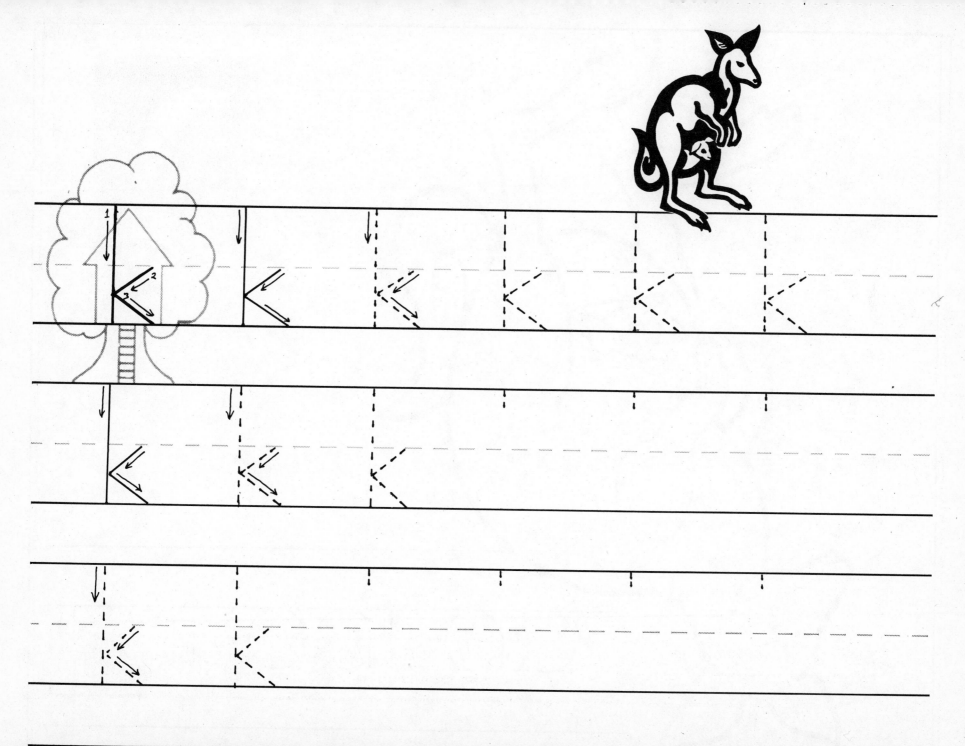

kangaroo

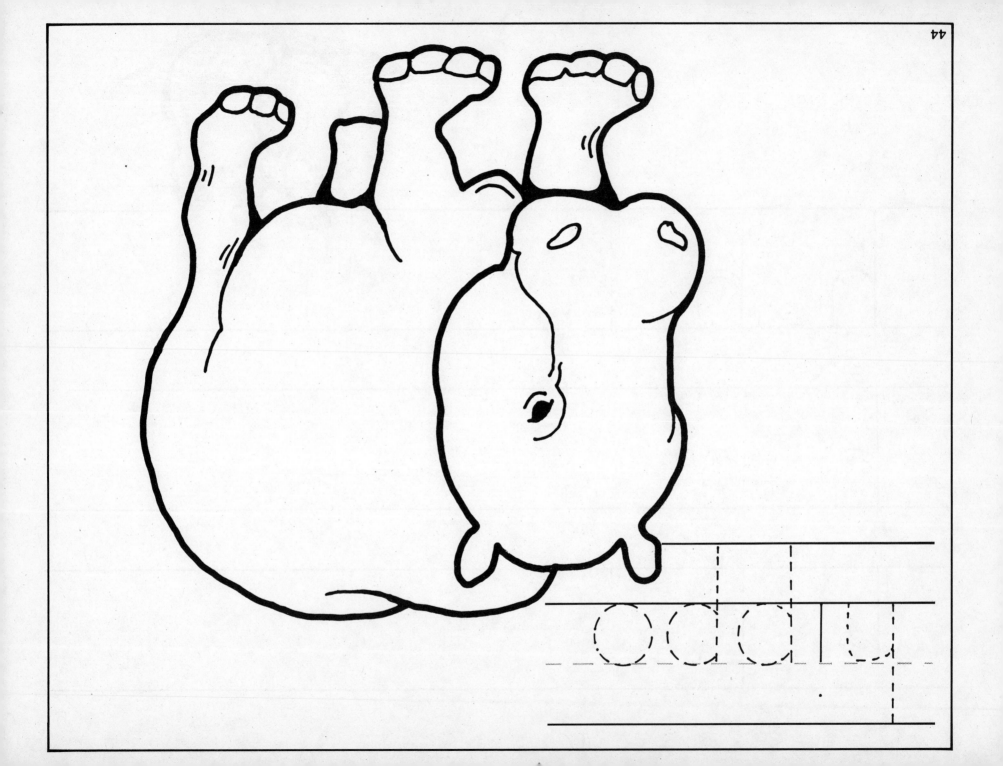

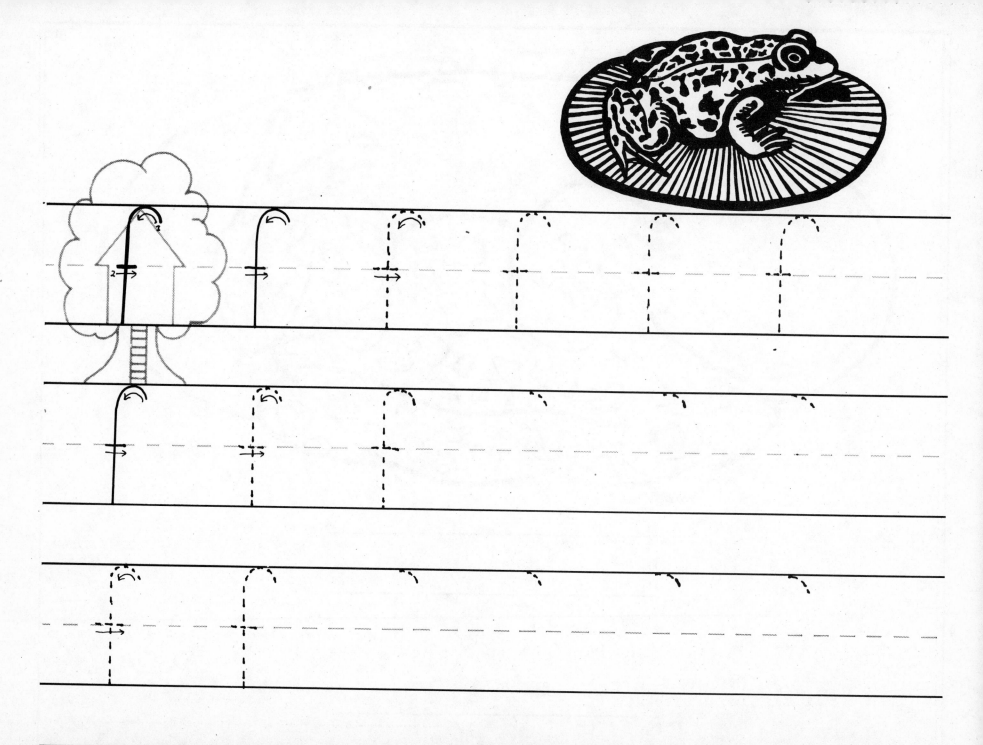

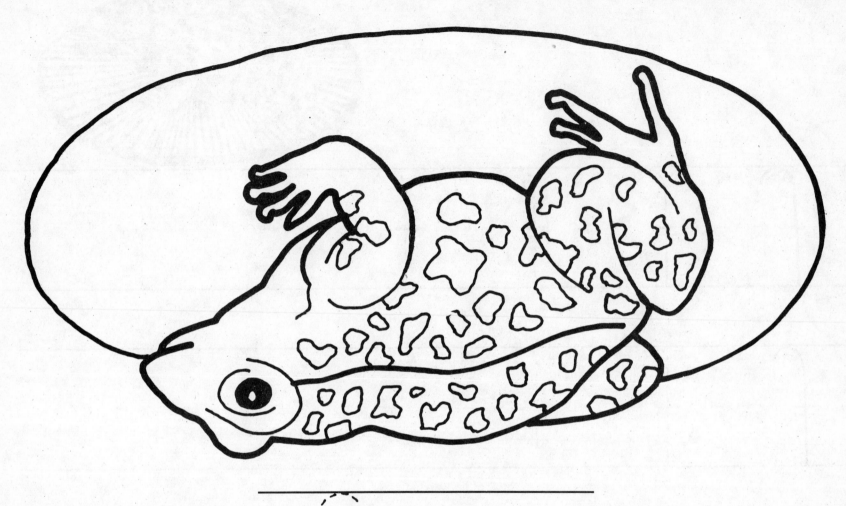

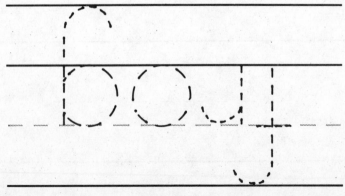

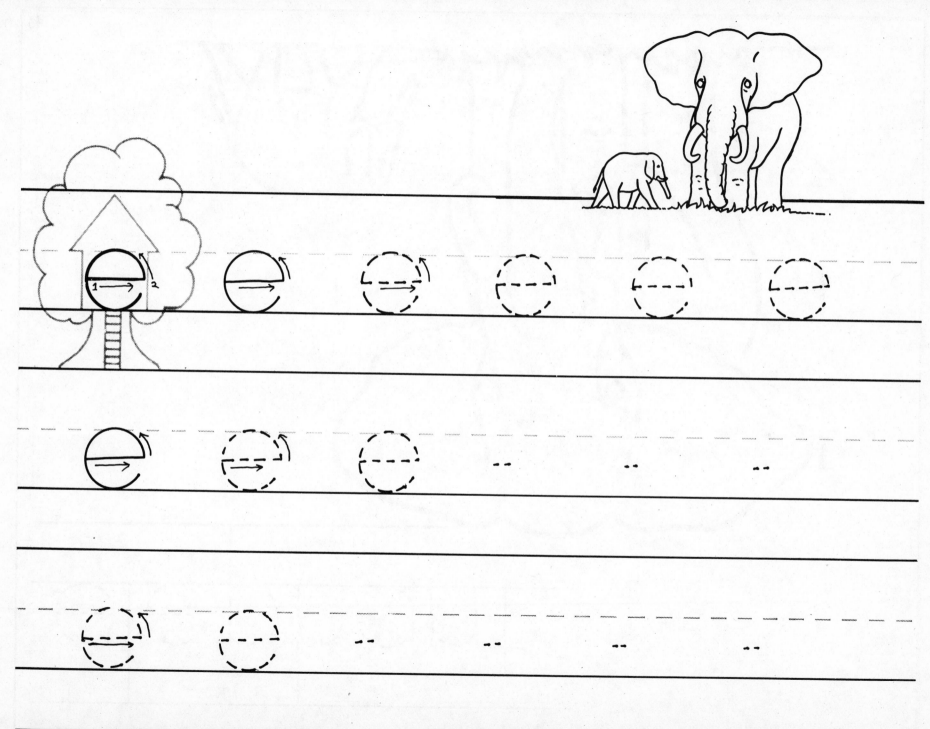

48

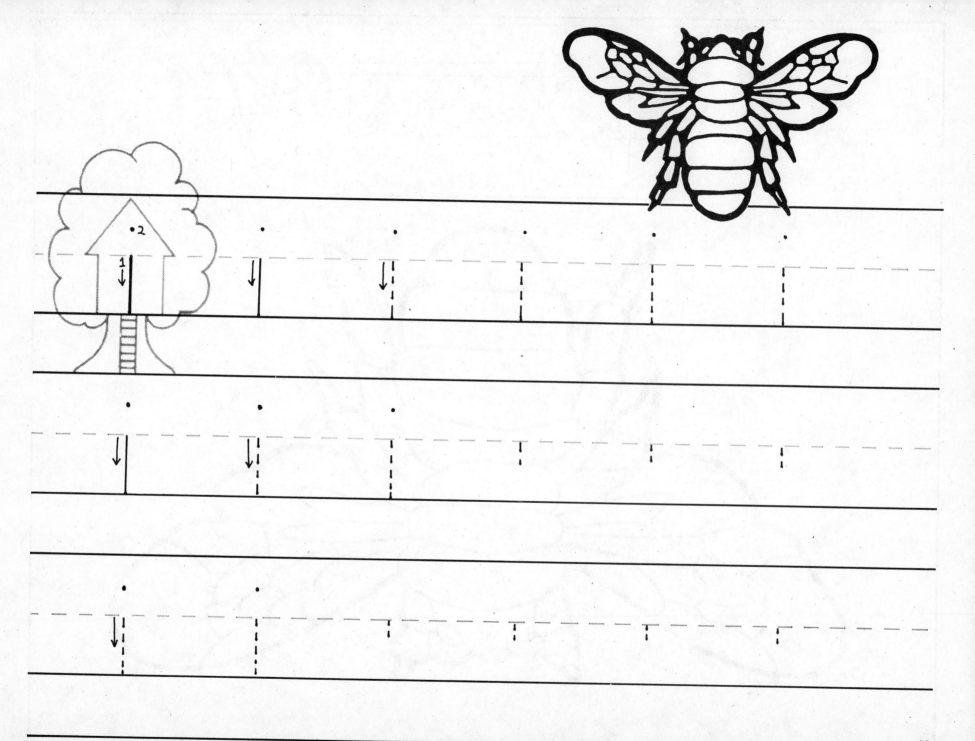

Insect

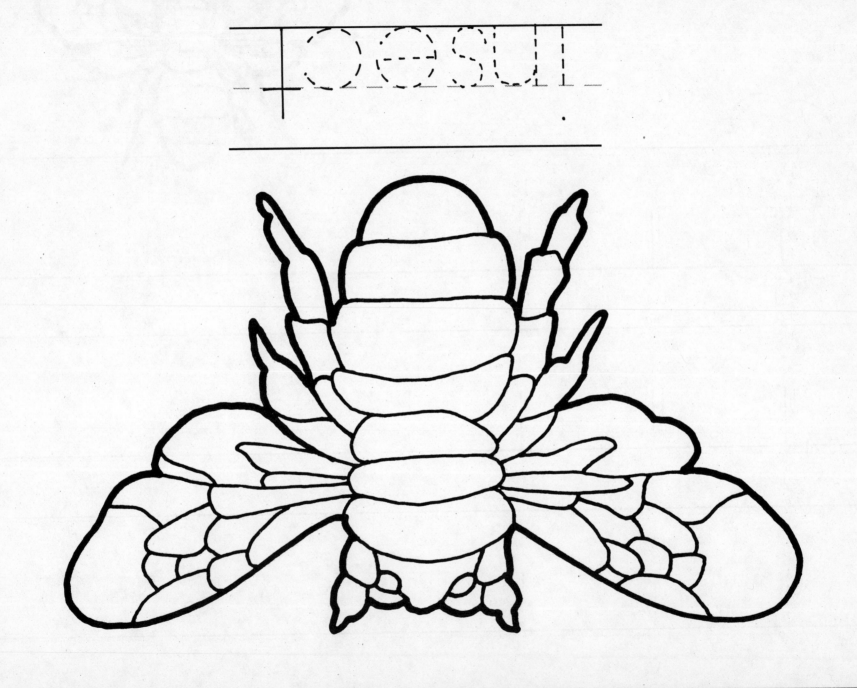

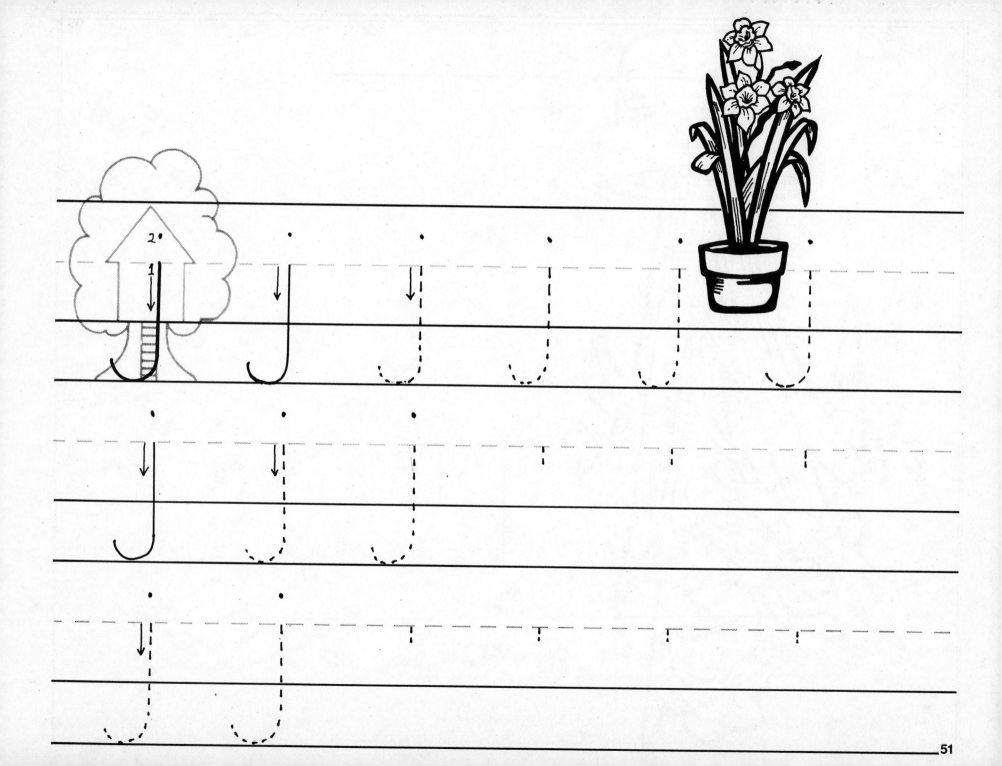

Draw a line from the picture to the correct letter.
Then fill the line with letters you make.

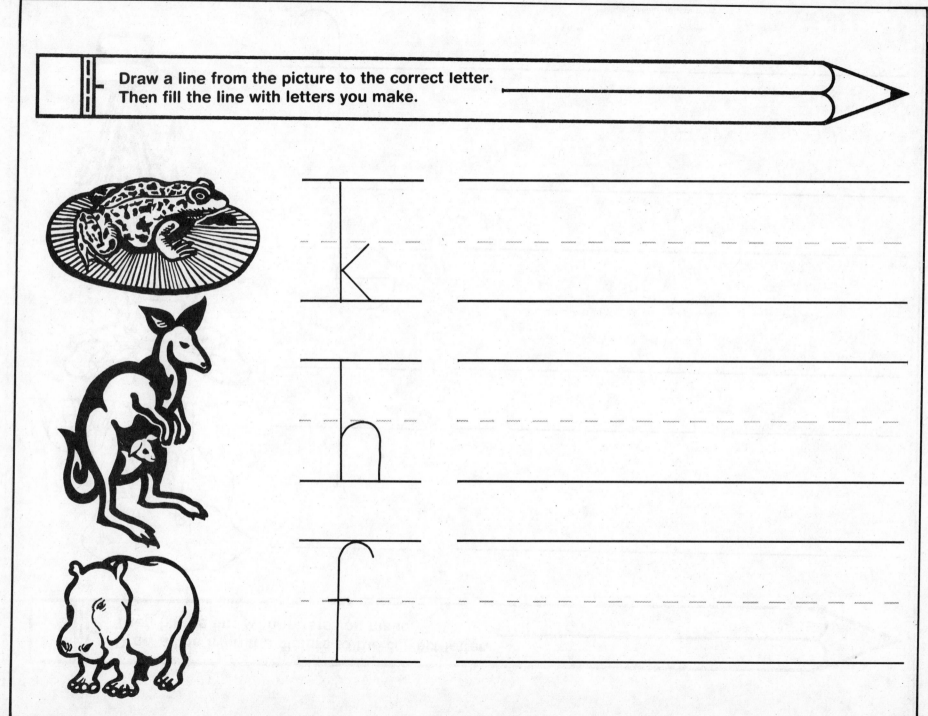

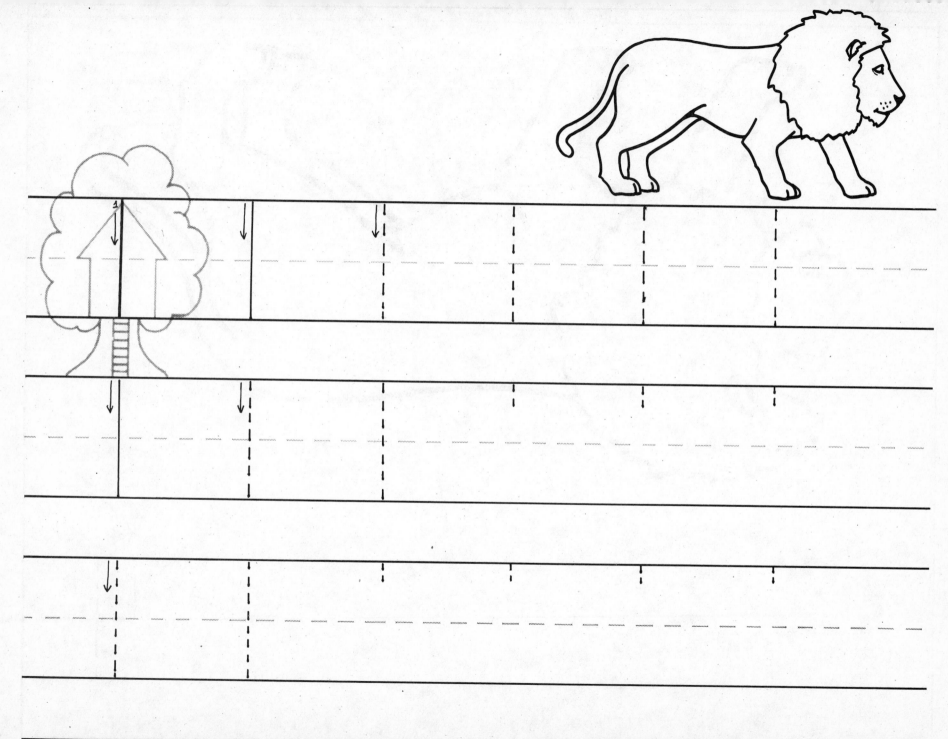

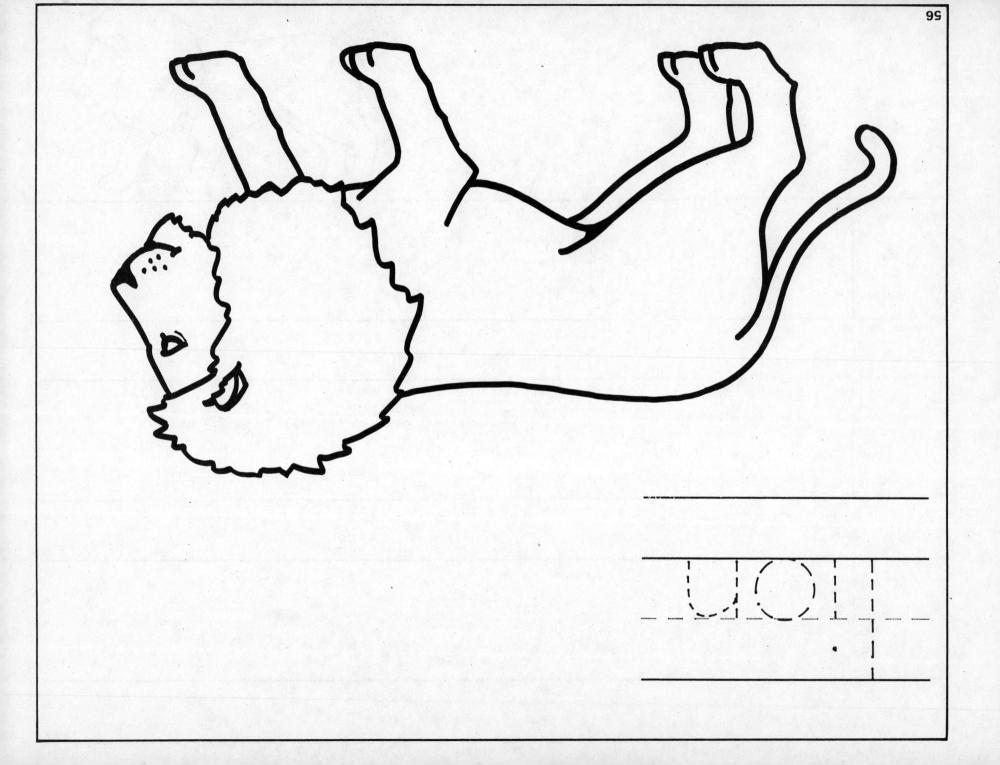

lion

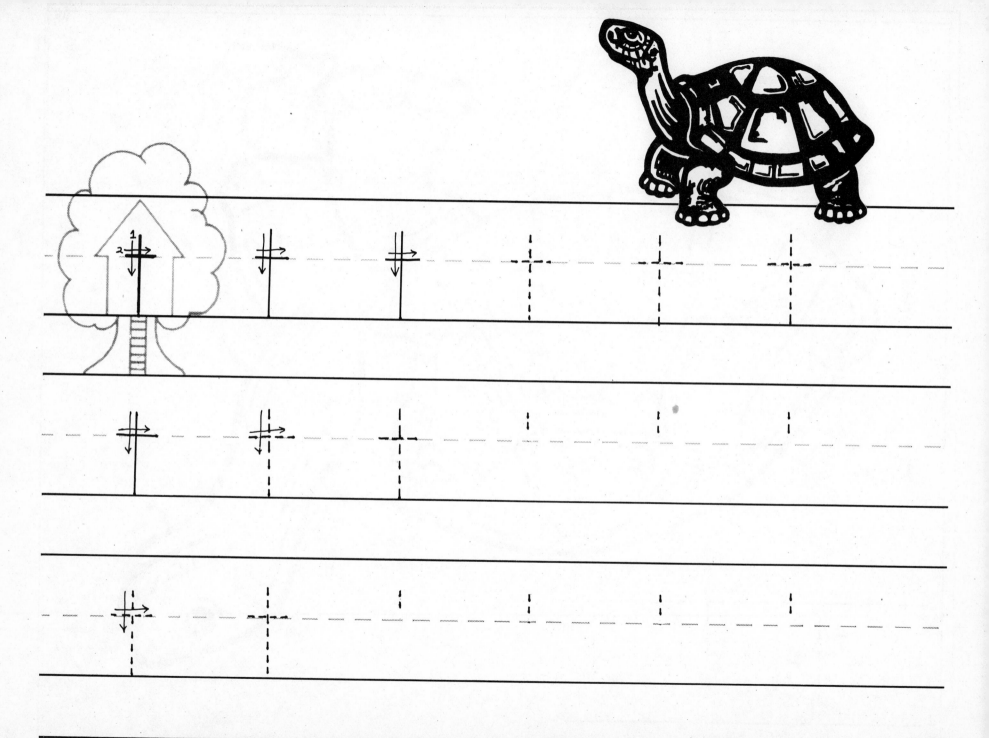

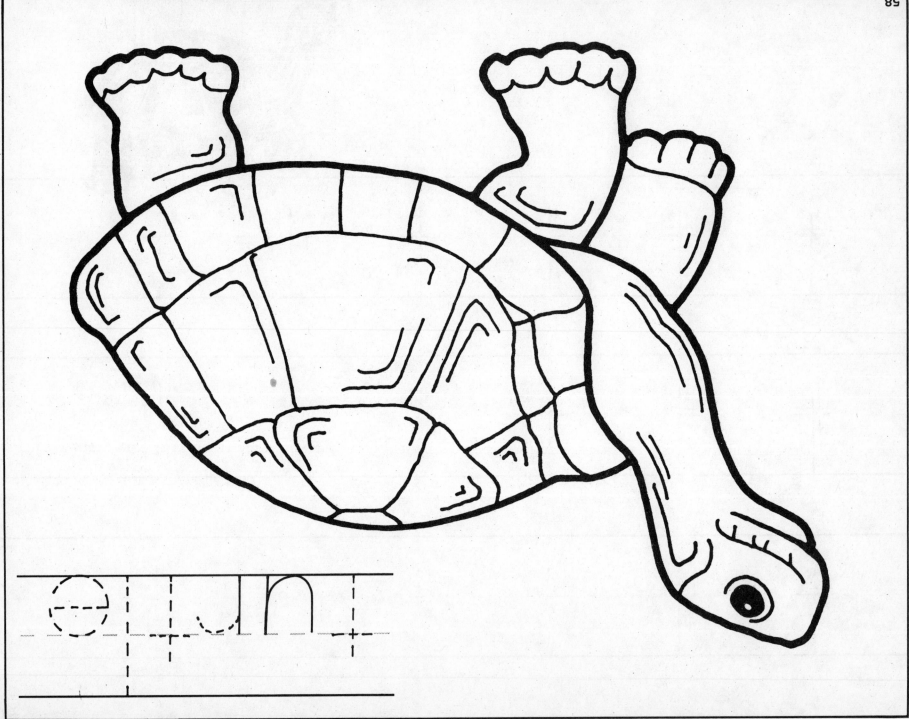

turtle

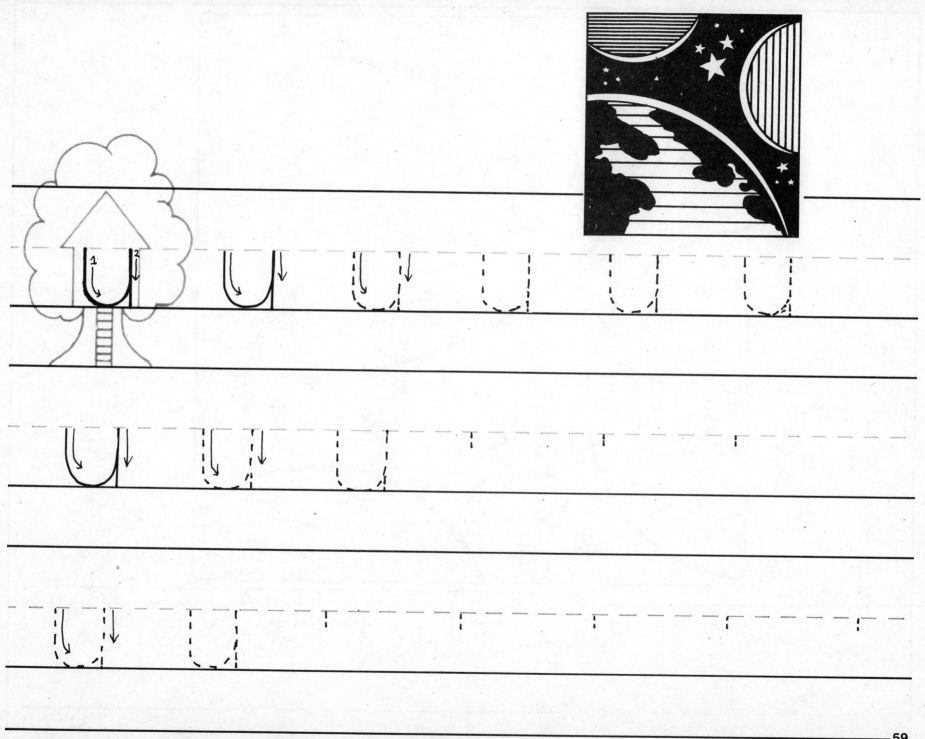

universe

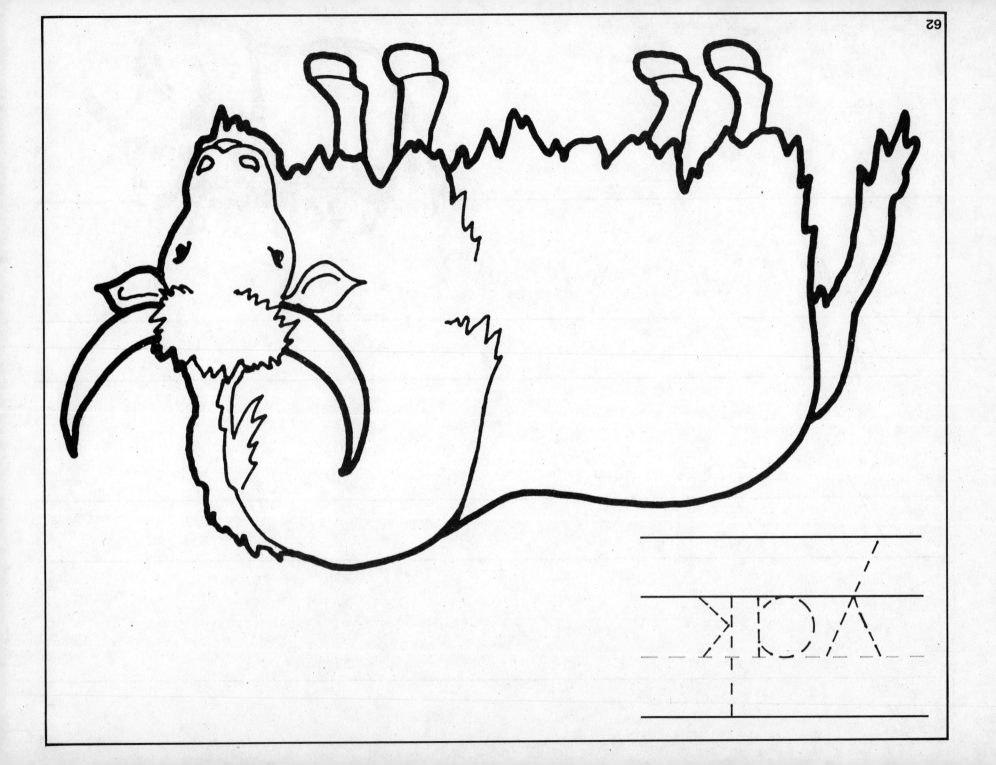

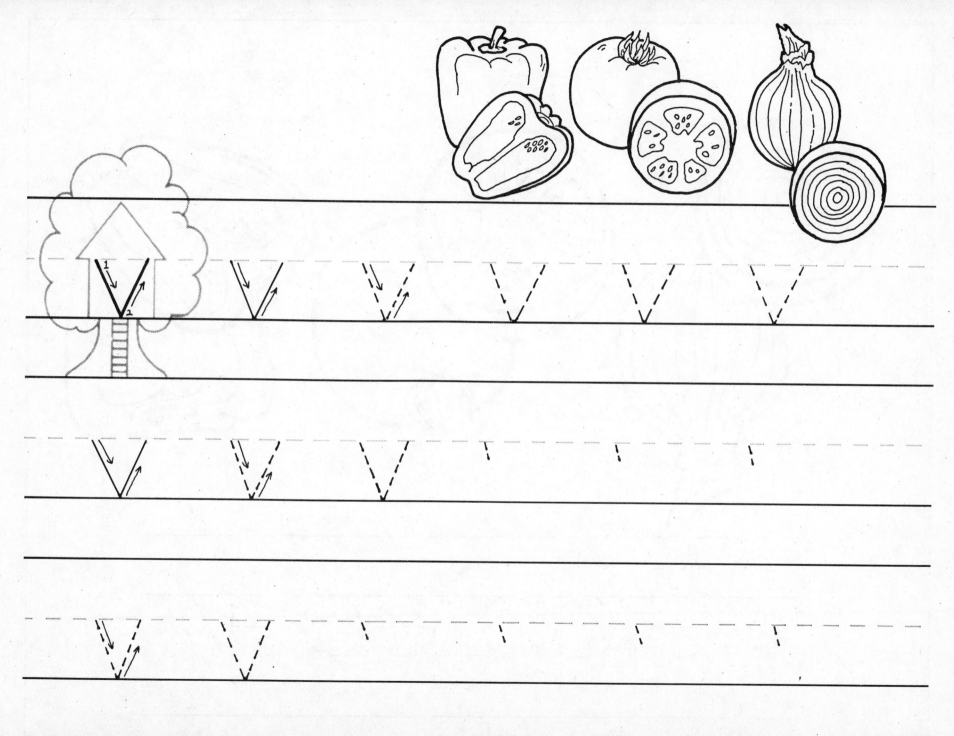

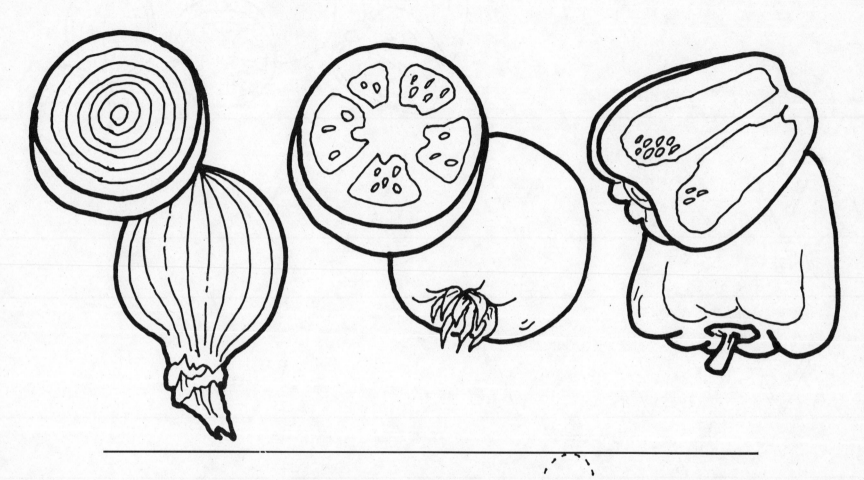

vegetables

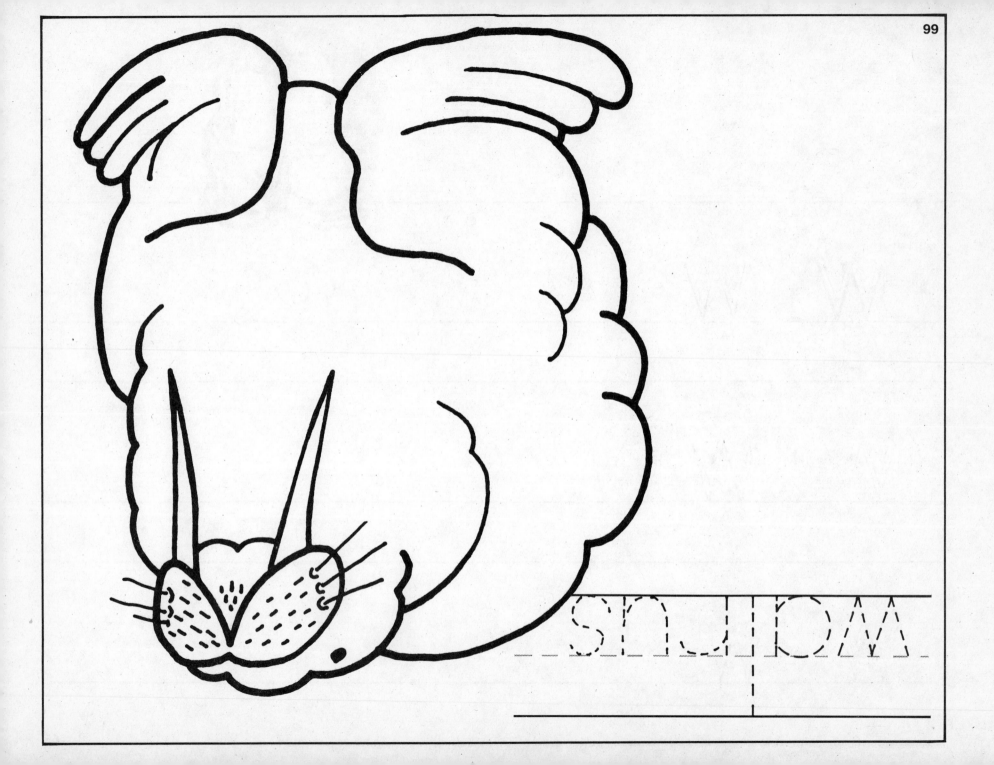

walrus

X as in ibex

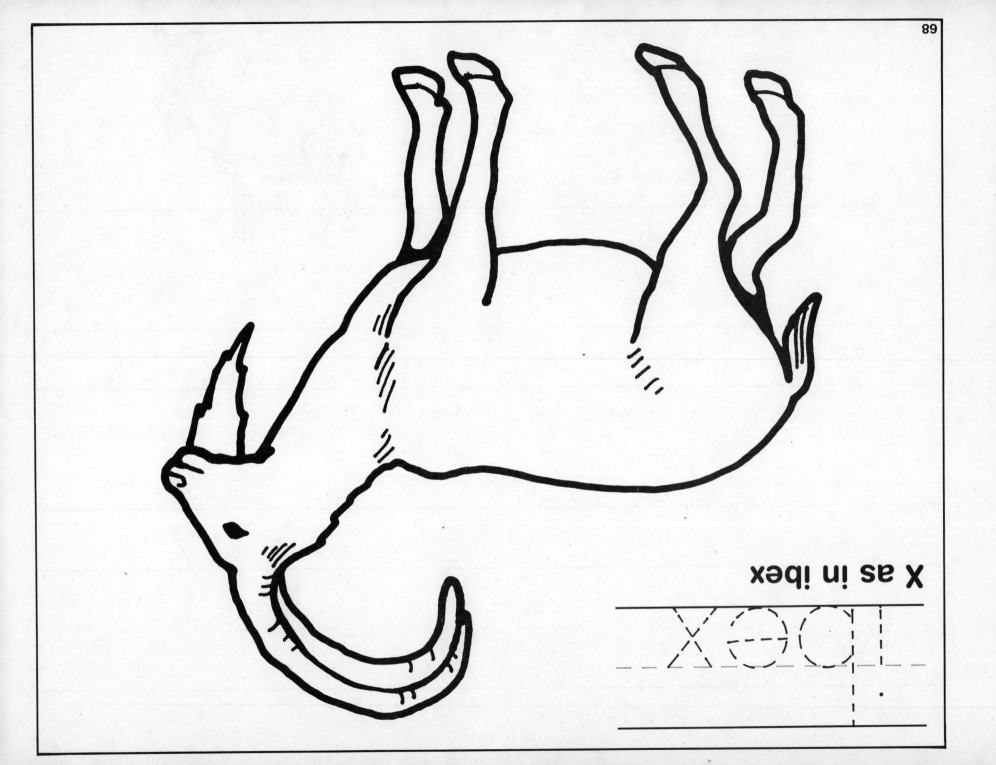

X as in ibex

ibex

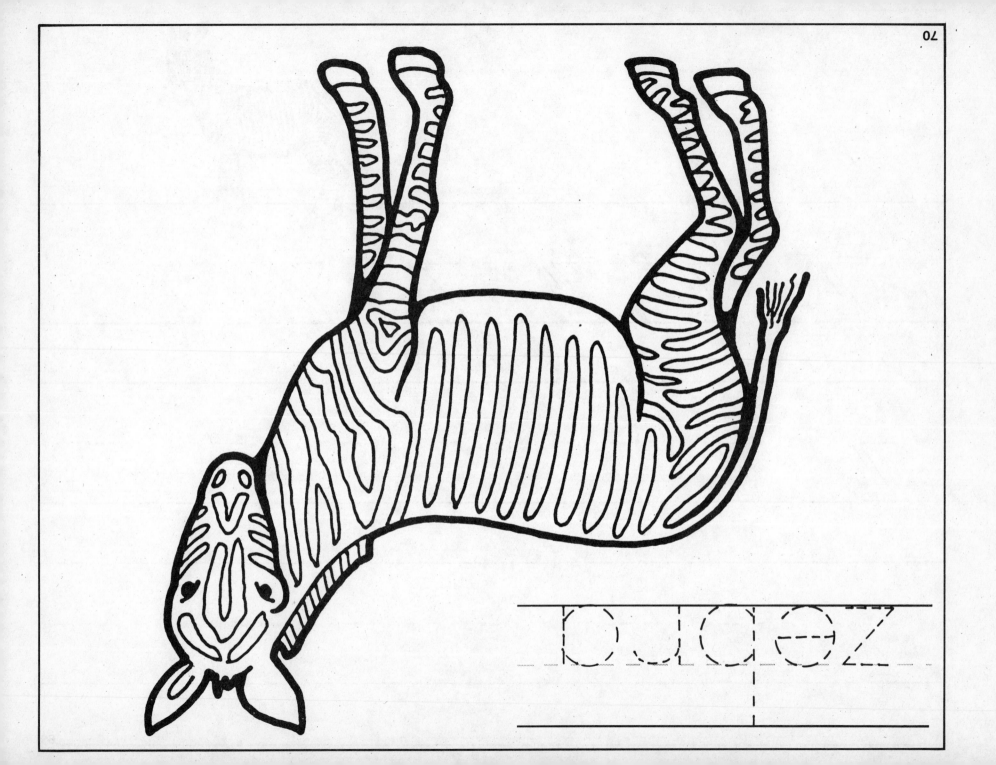

zebra

Draw a line from the picture to the correct letter.
Then fill the line with letters you make.

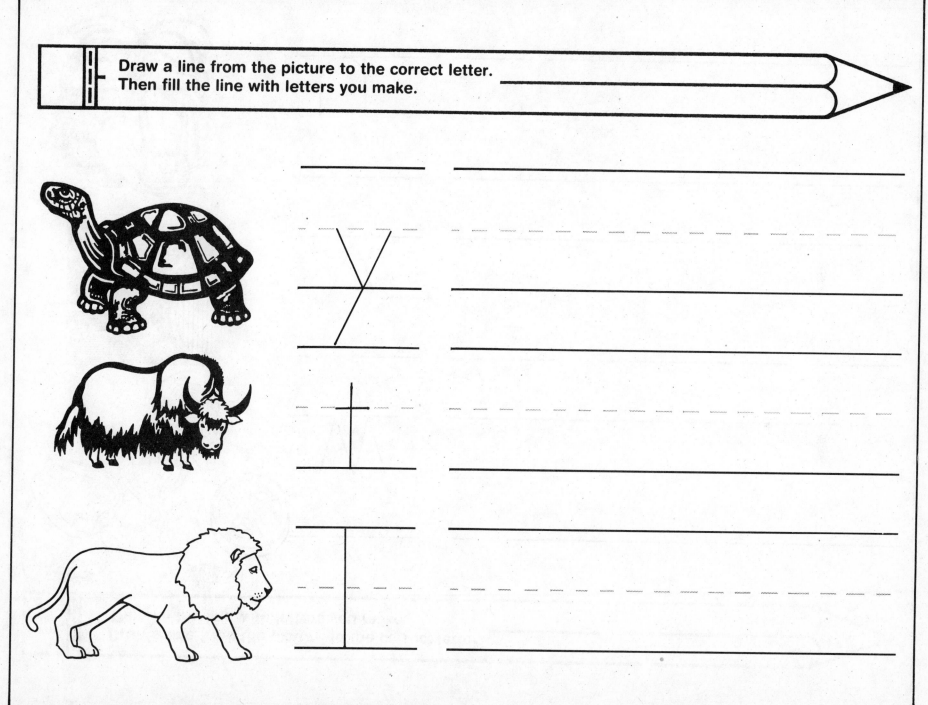

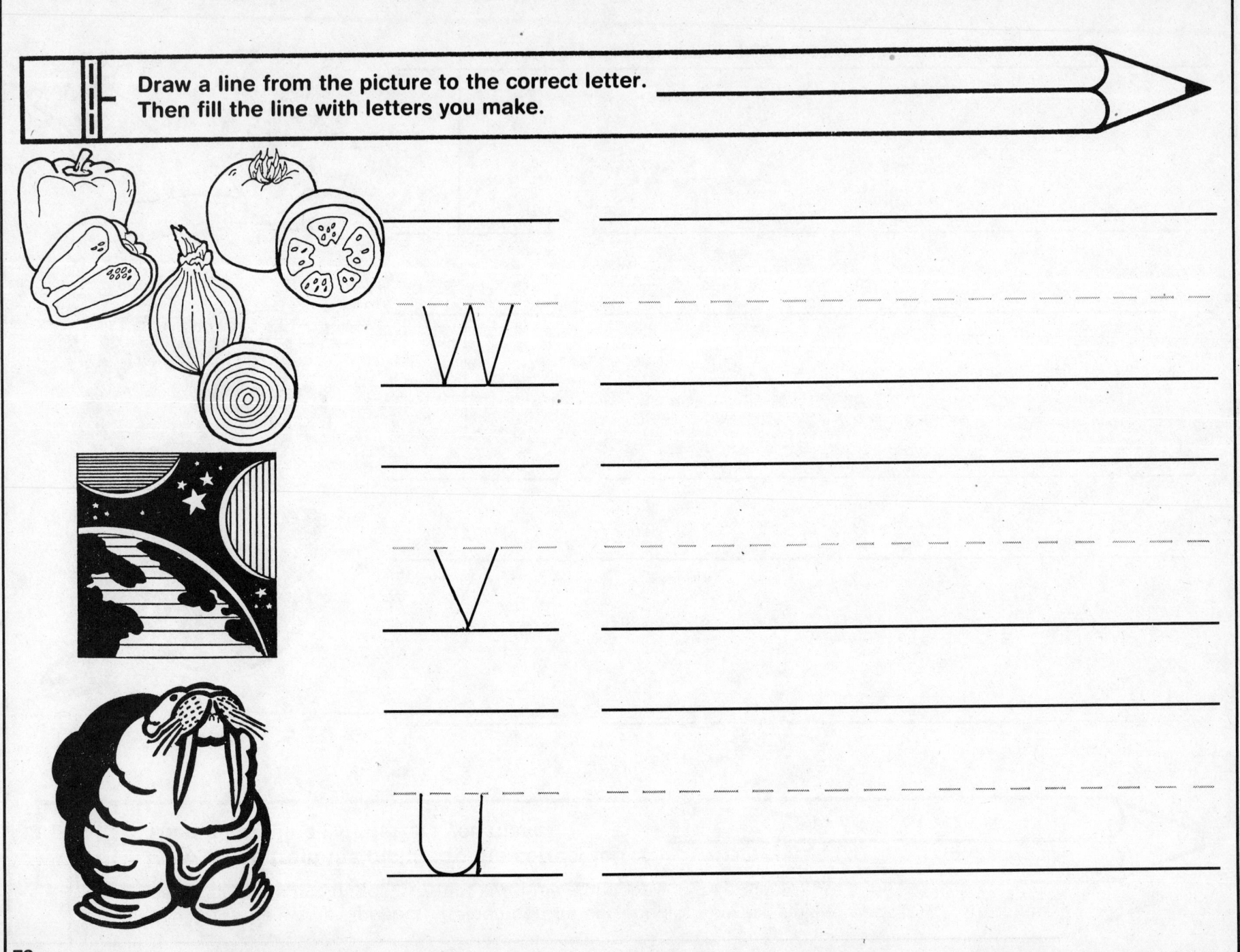

Draw a line from the picture to the correct letter.
Then fill the line with letters you make.

W

V

U

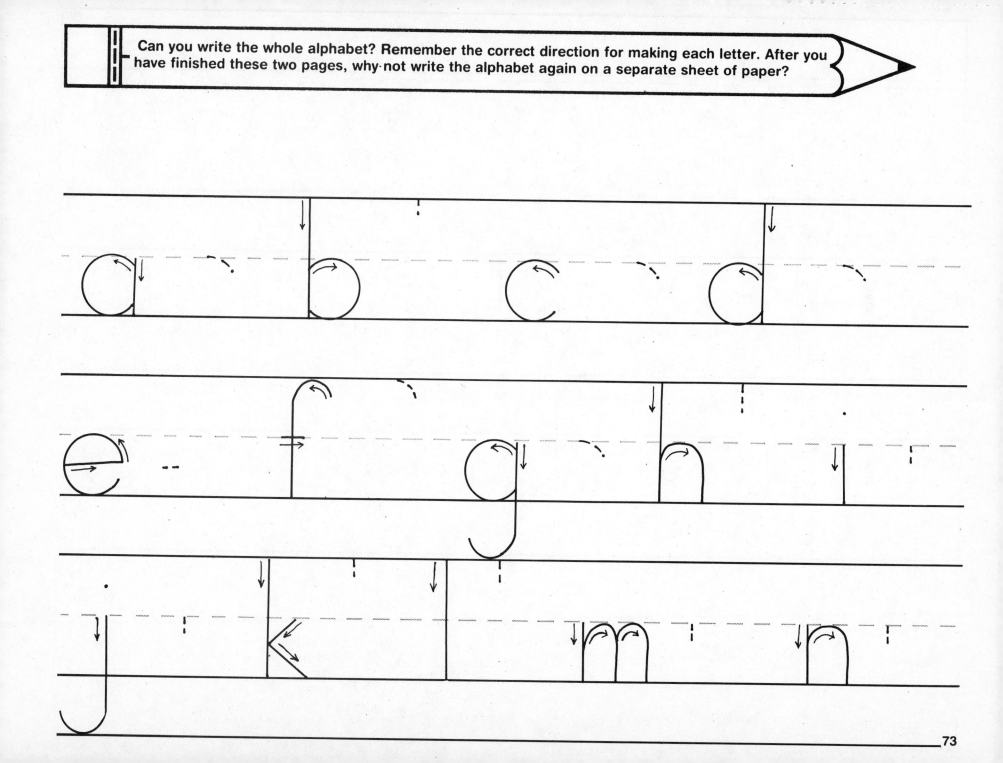

Can you write the whole alphabet? Remember the correct direction for making each letter. After you have finished these two pages, why not write the alphabet again on a separate sheet of paper?

73

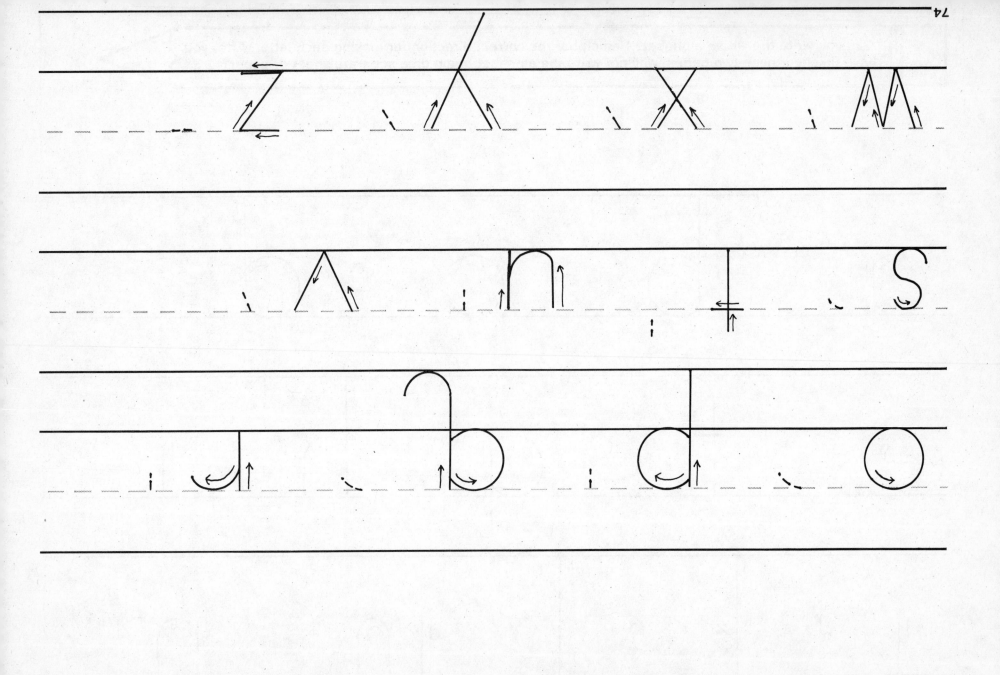

Draw a line from the picture to the correct letter.
Then fill the line with letters you make.

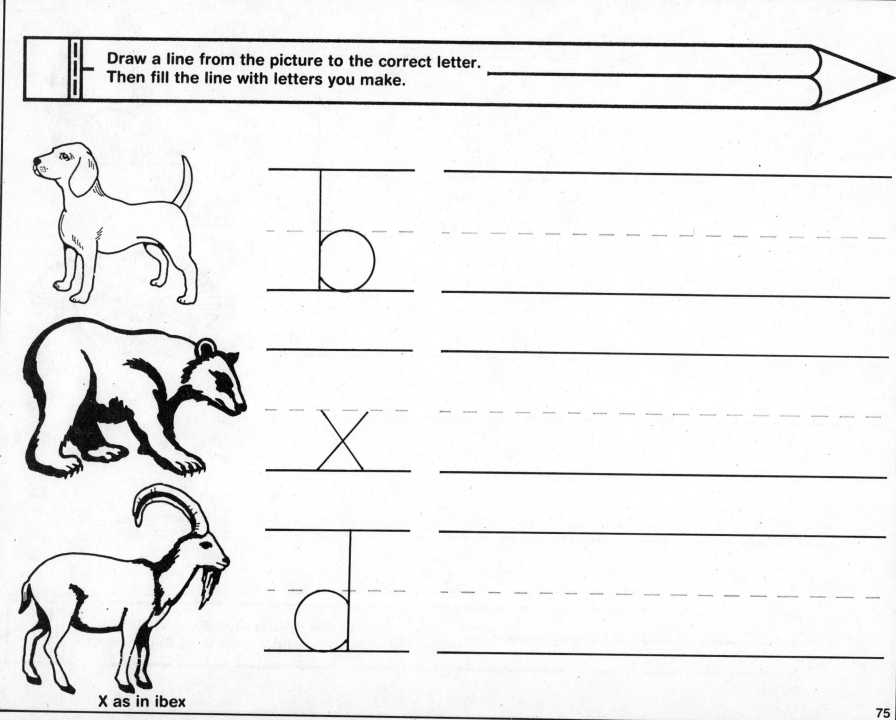

X as in ibex

75

Draw a line from the picture to the correct letter.
Then fill the line with letters you make.

z

r

f

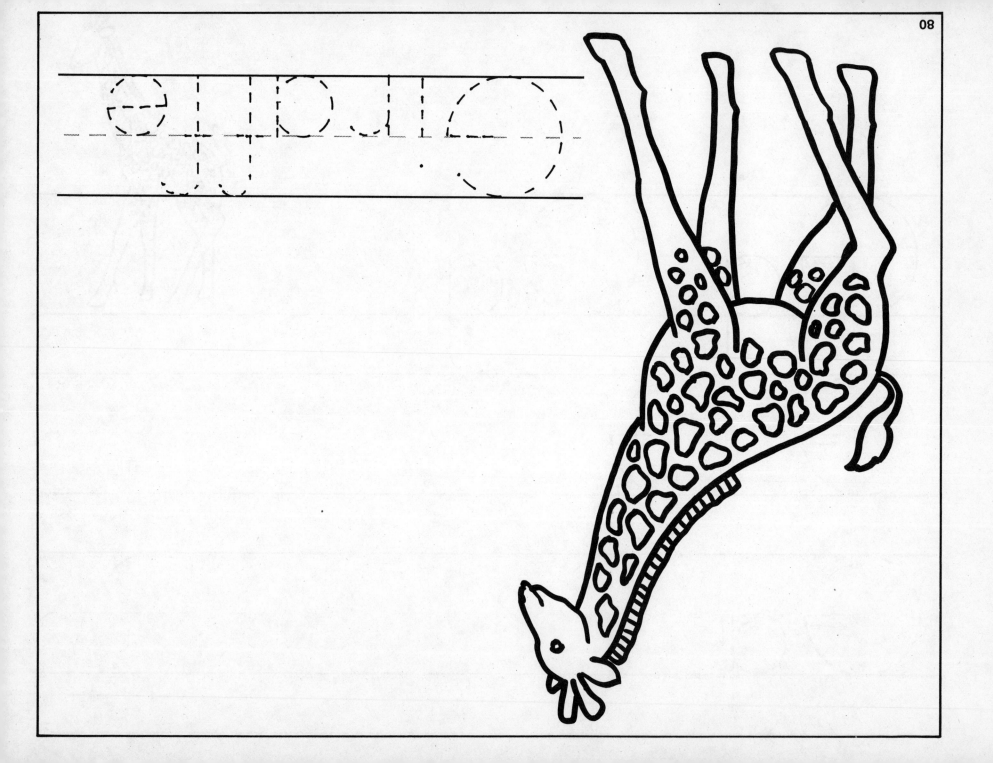

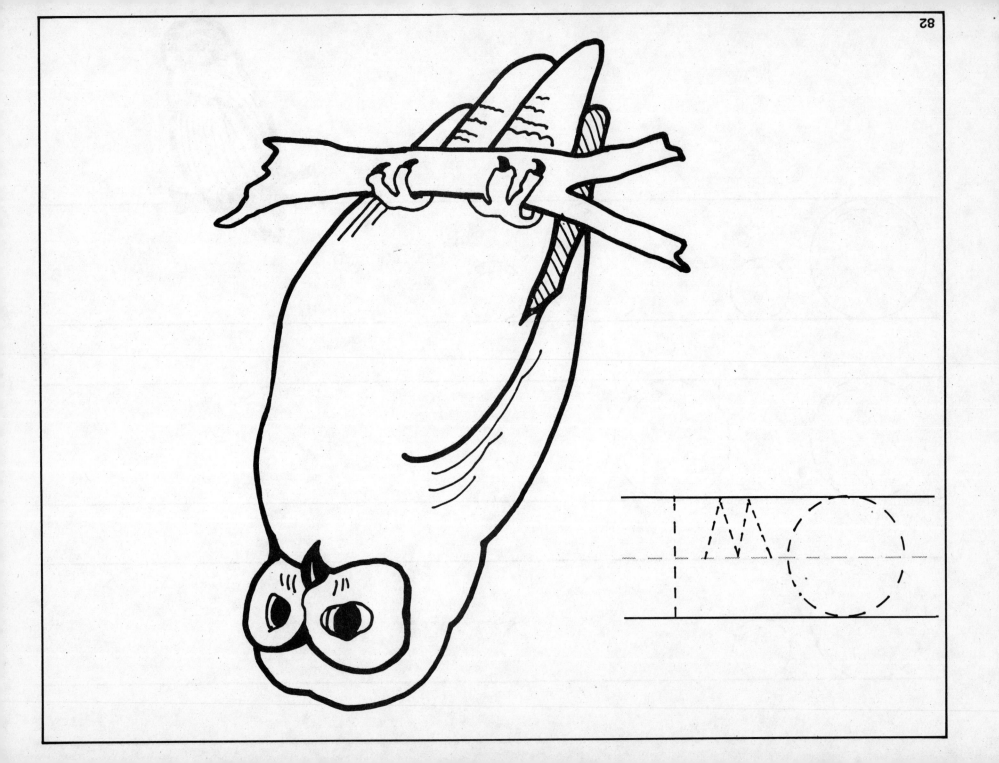

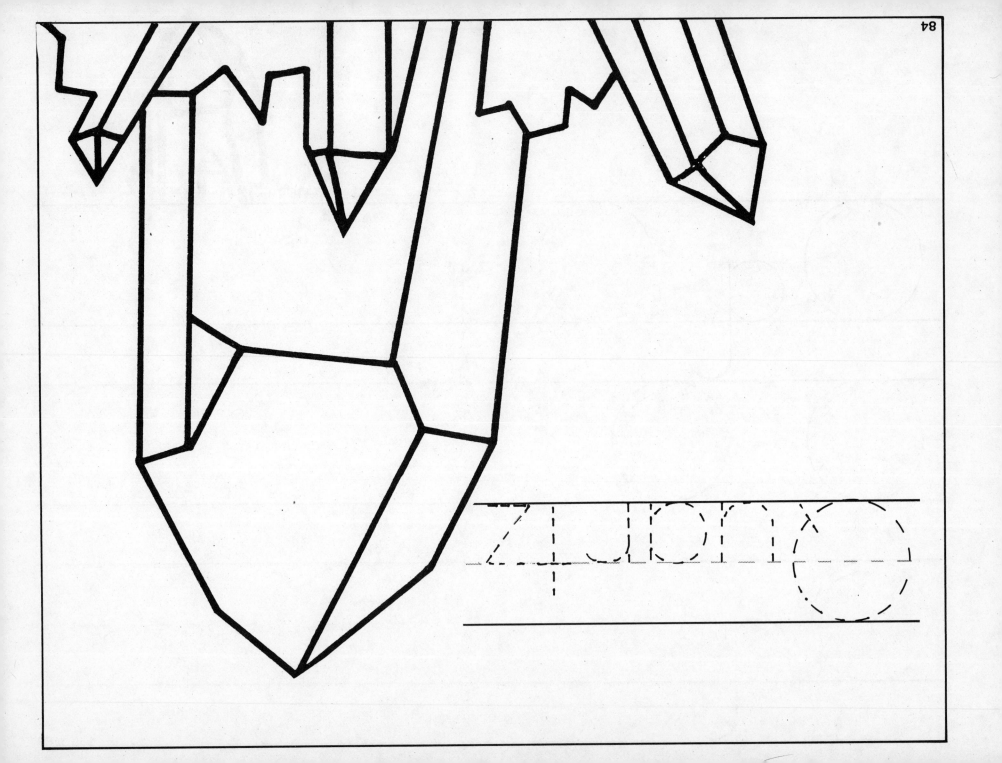

S s S s S s

S S

S s

uns

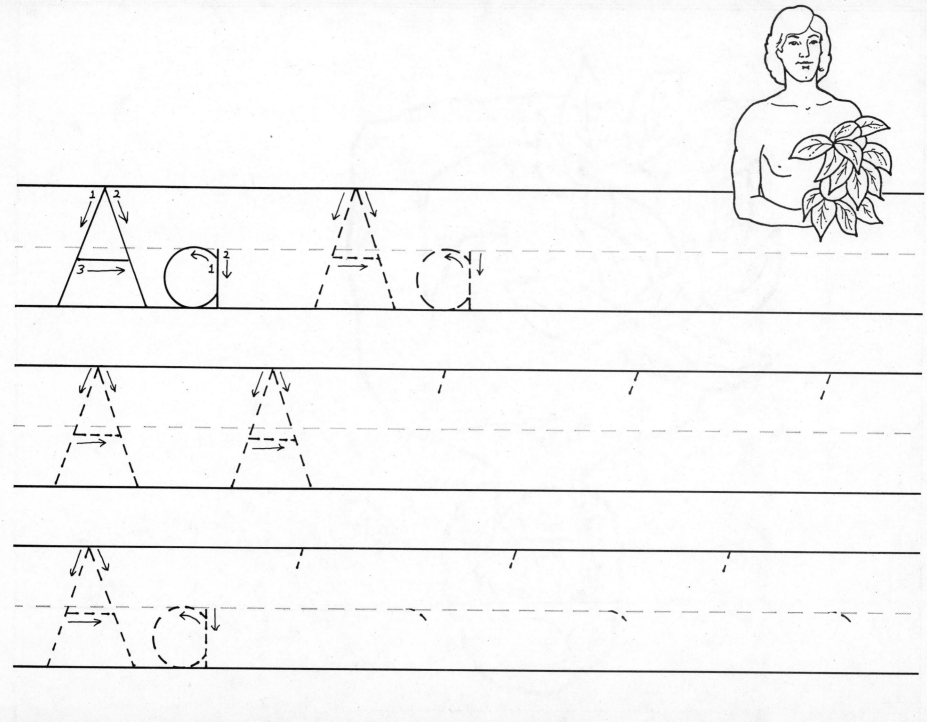

Acorn

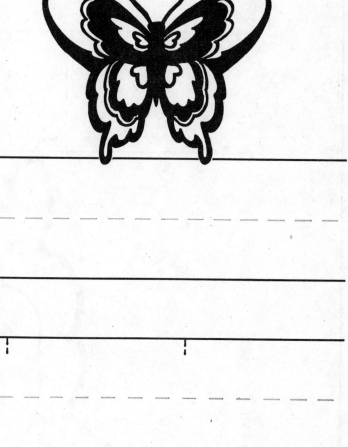

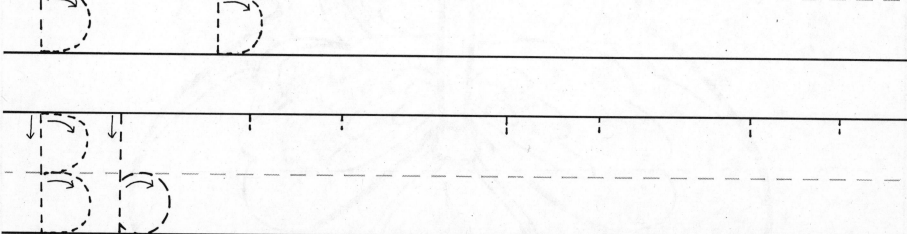

Butterfly

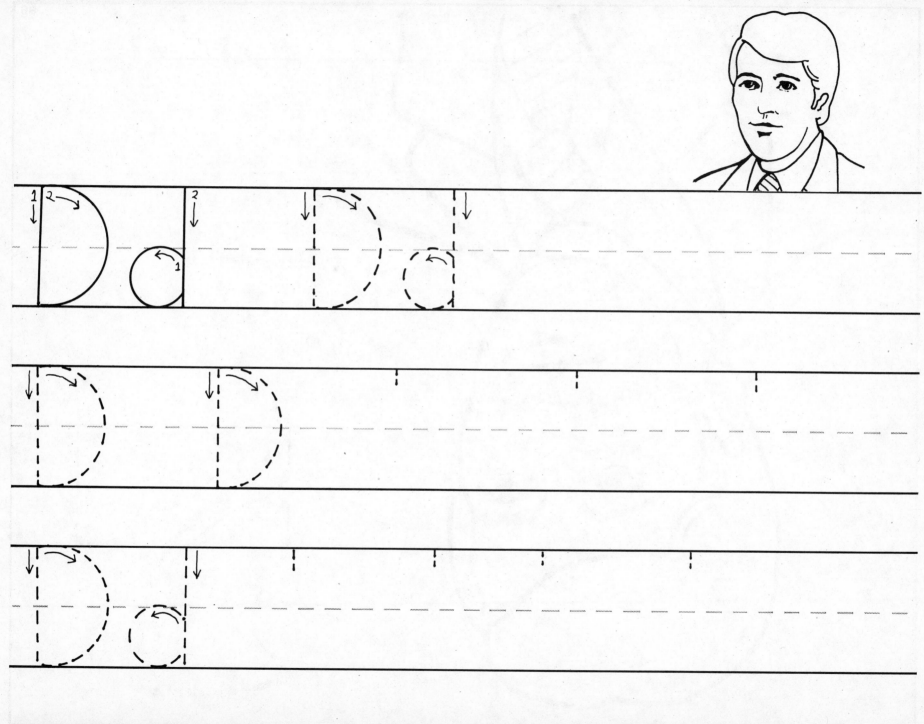

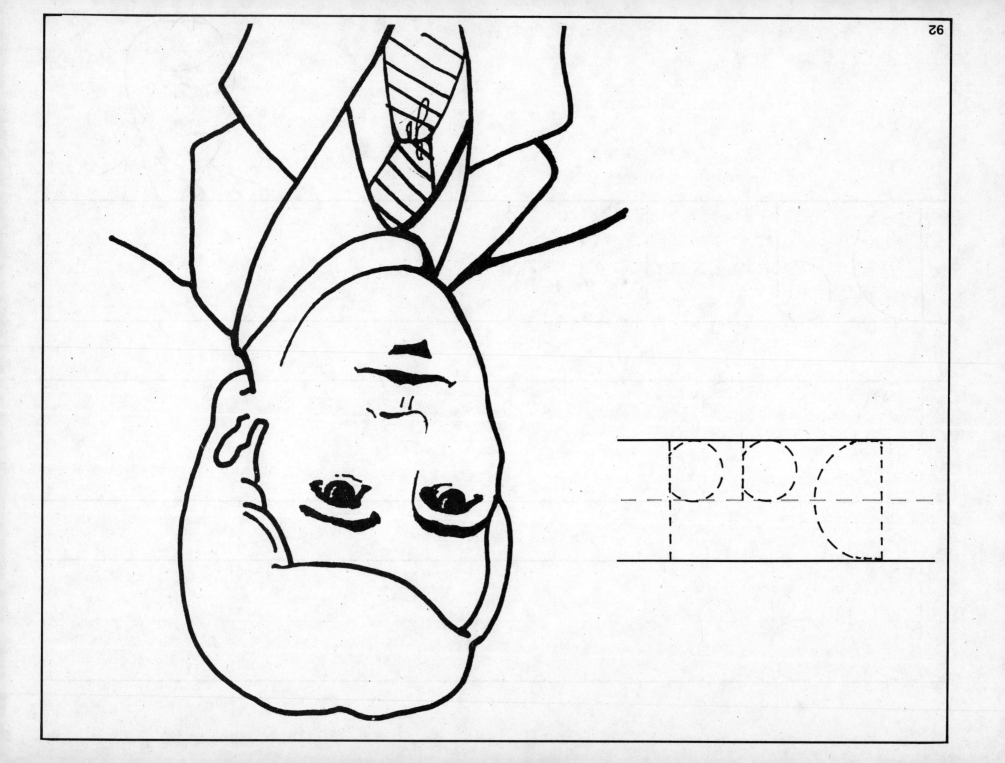

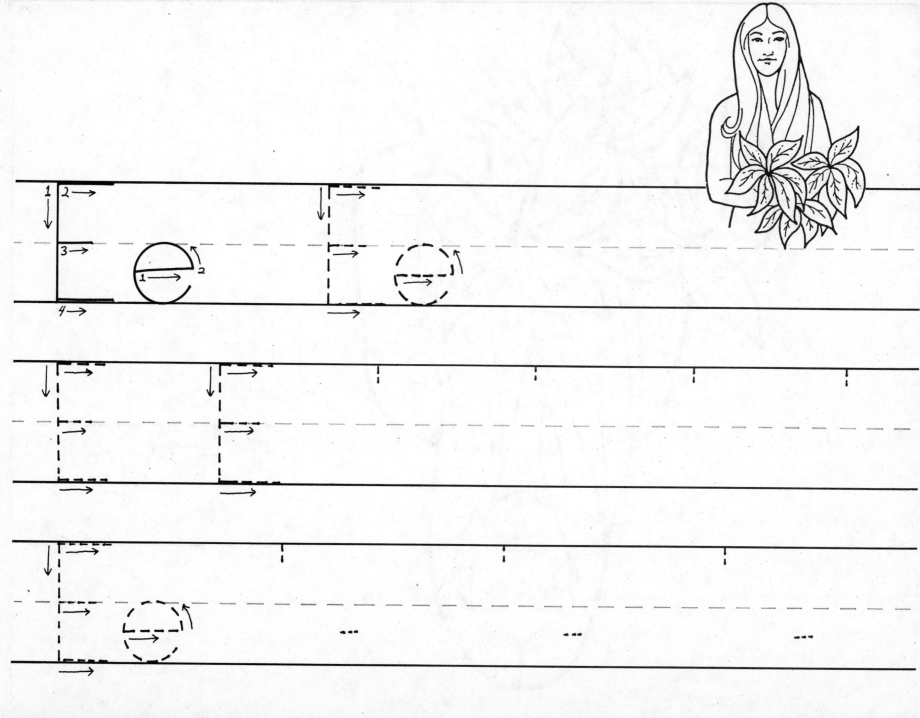

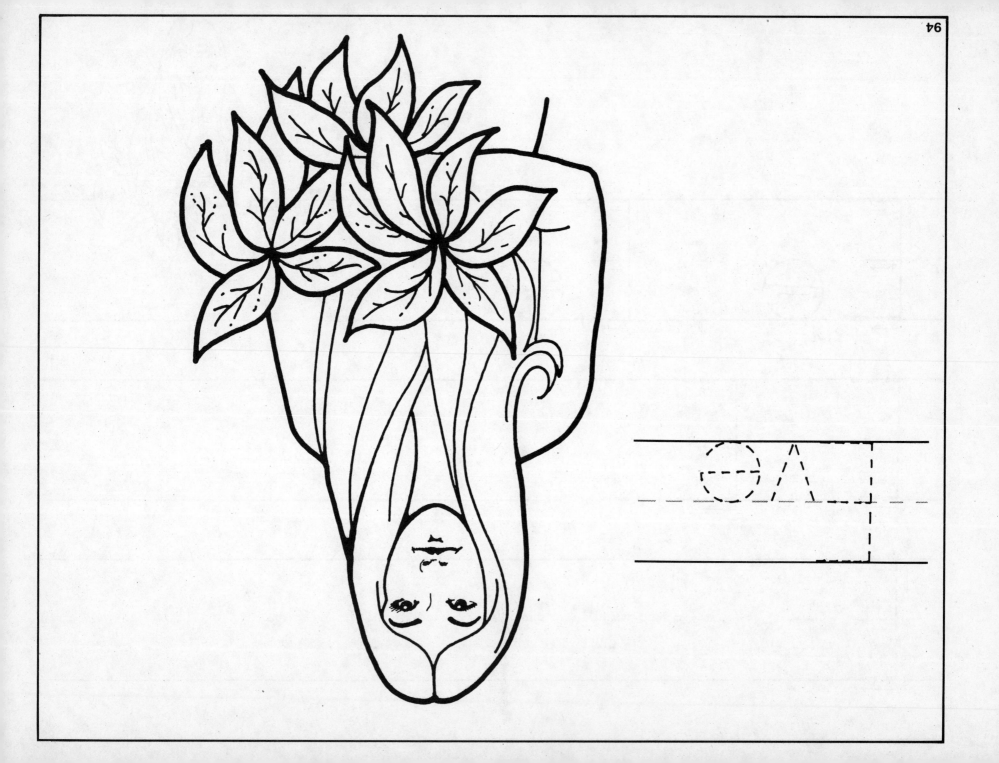

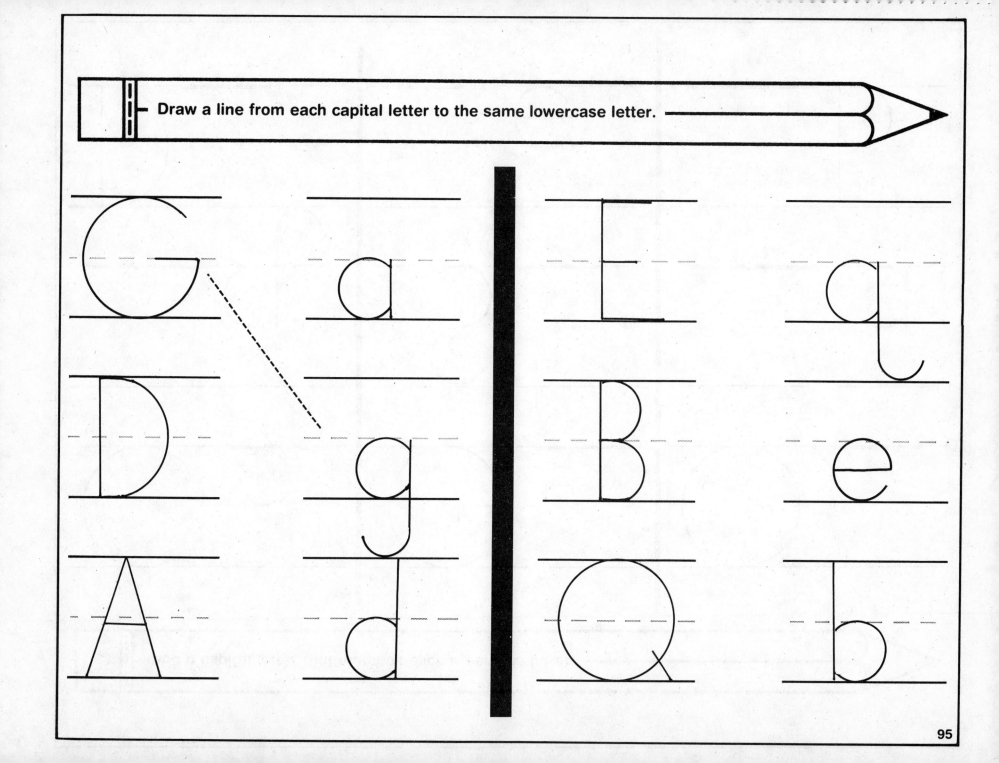

Draw a line from each capital letter to the same lowercase letter.

95

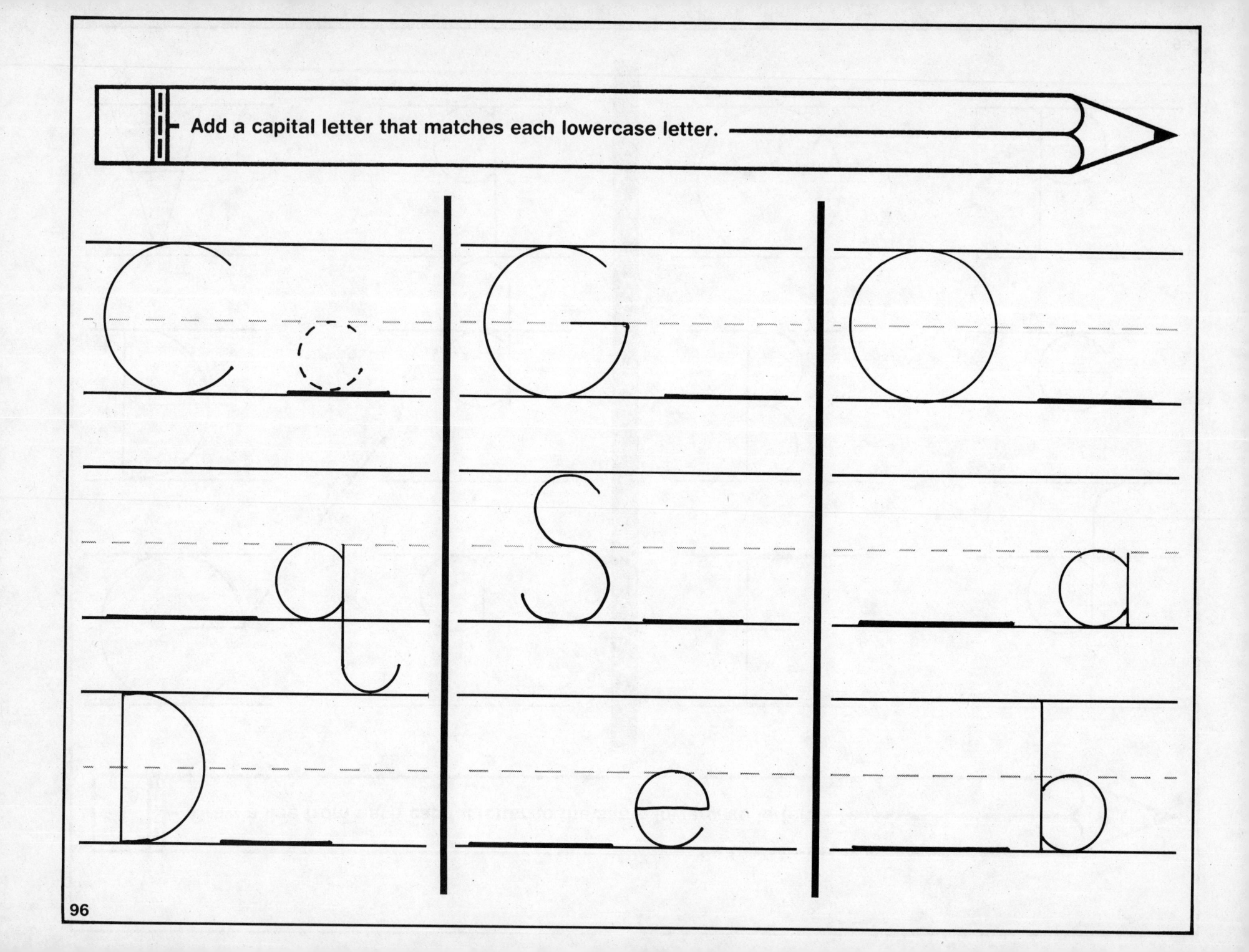

C c

G g

O o

a

S s

a

D

e

b

96

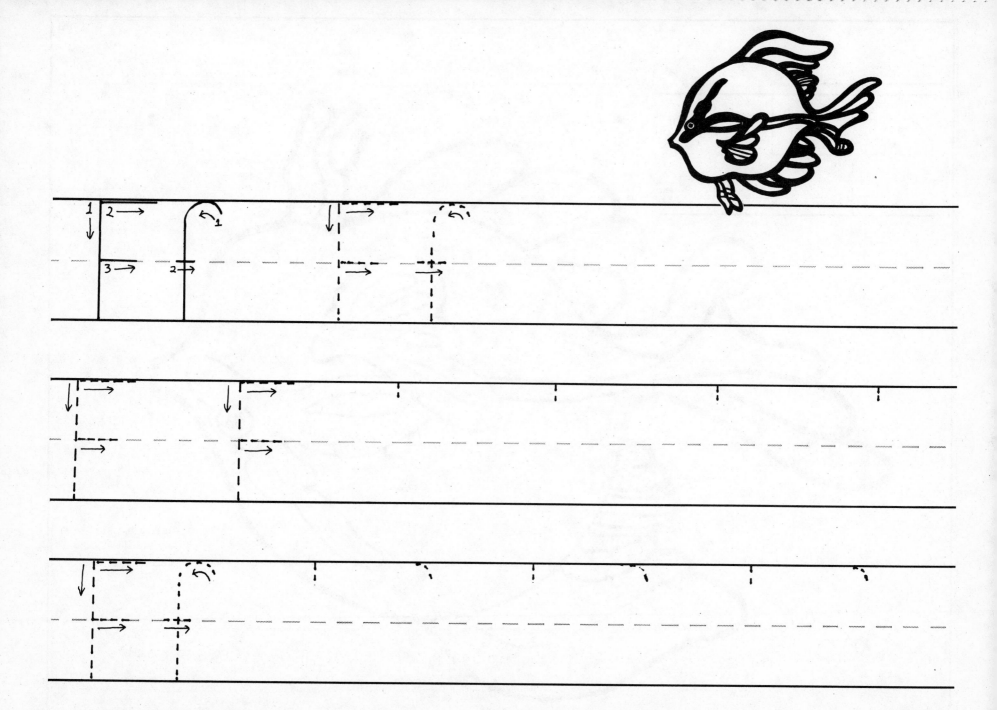

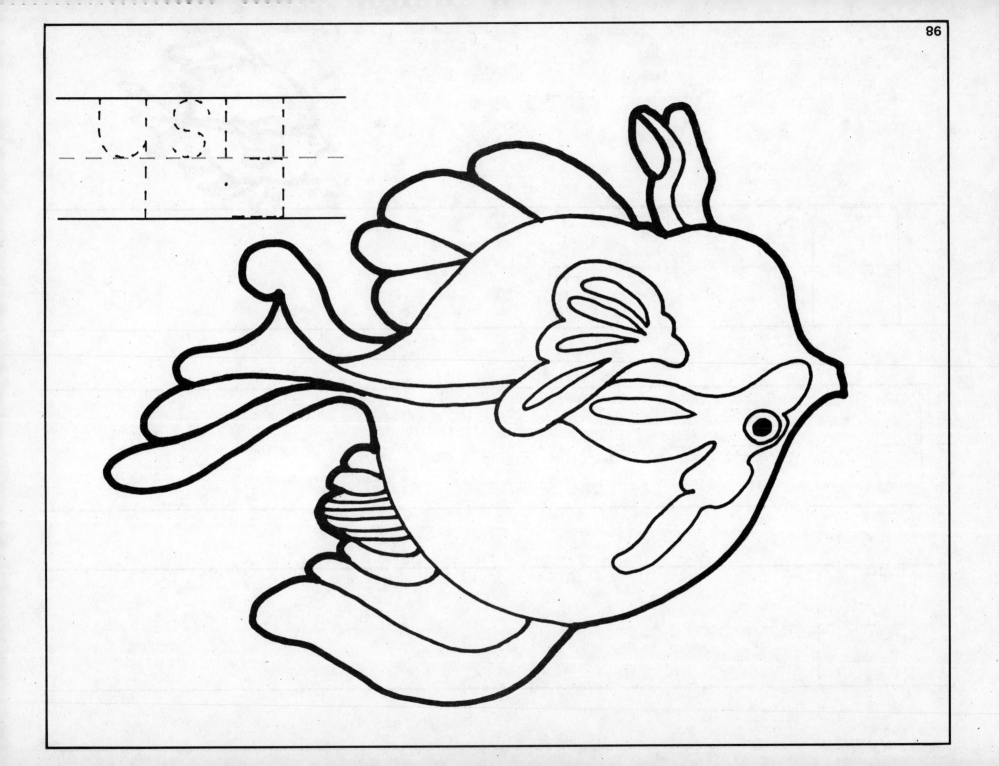

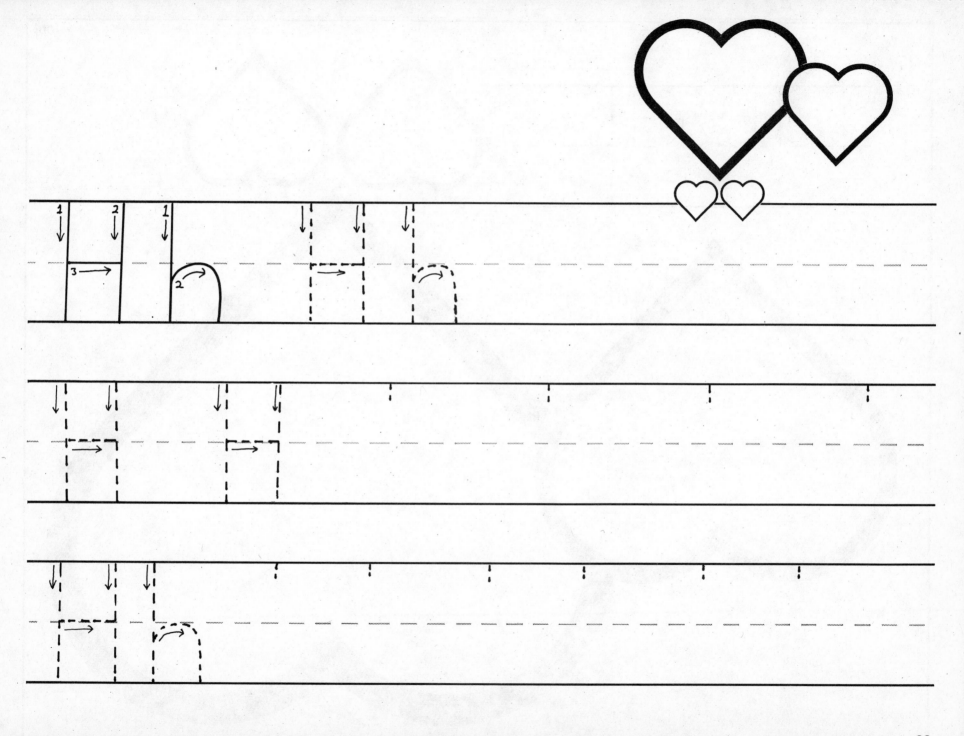

Heart

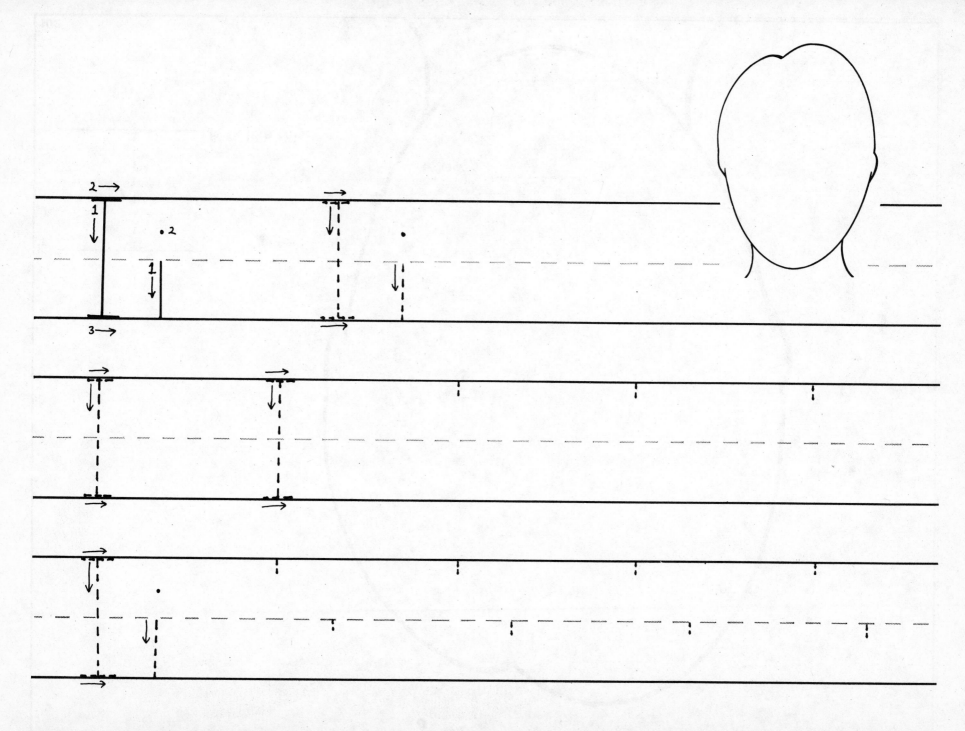

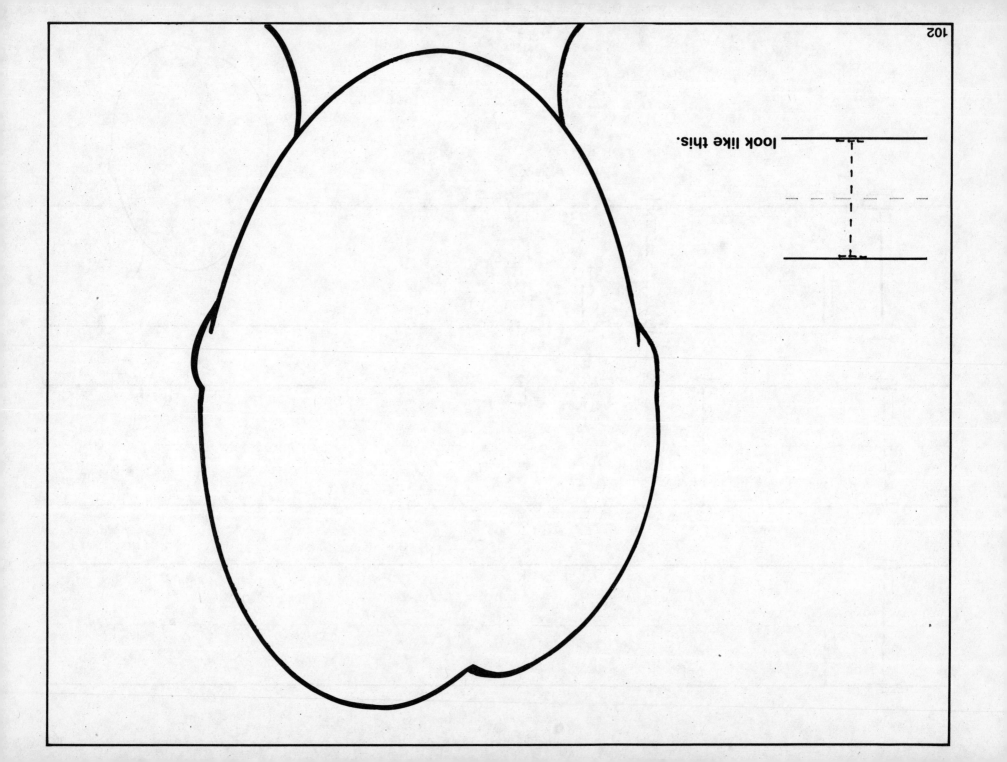

look like this.

Jesus

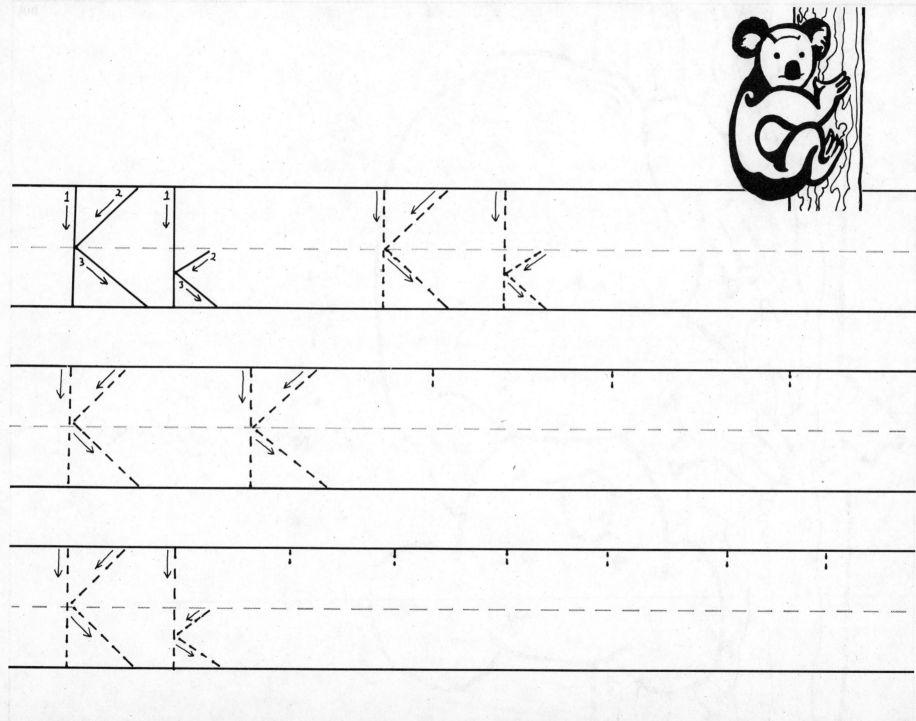

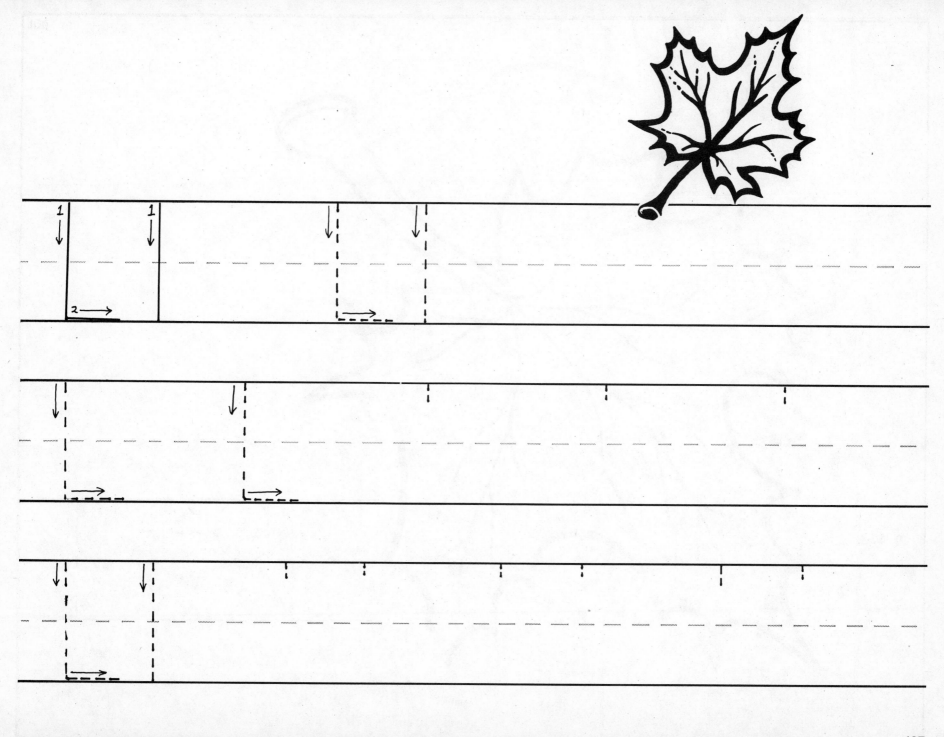

Leaf

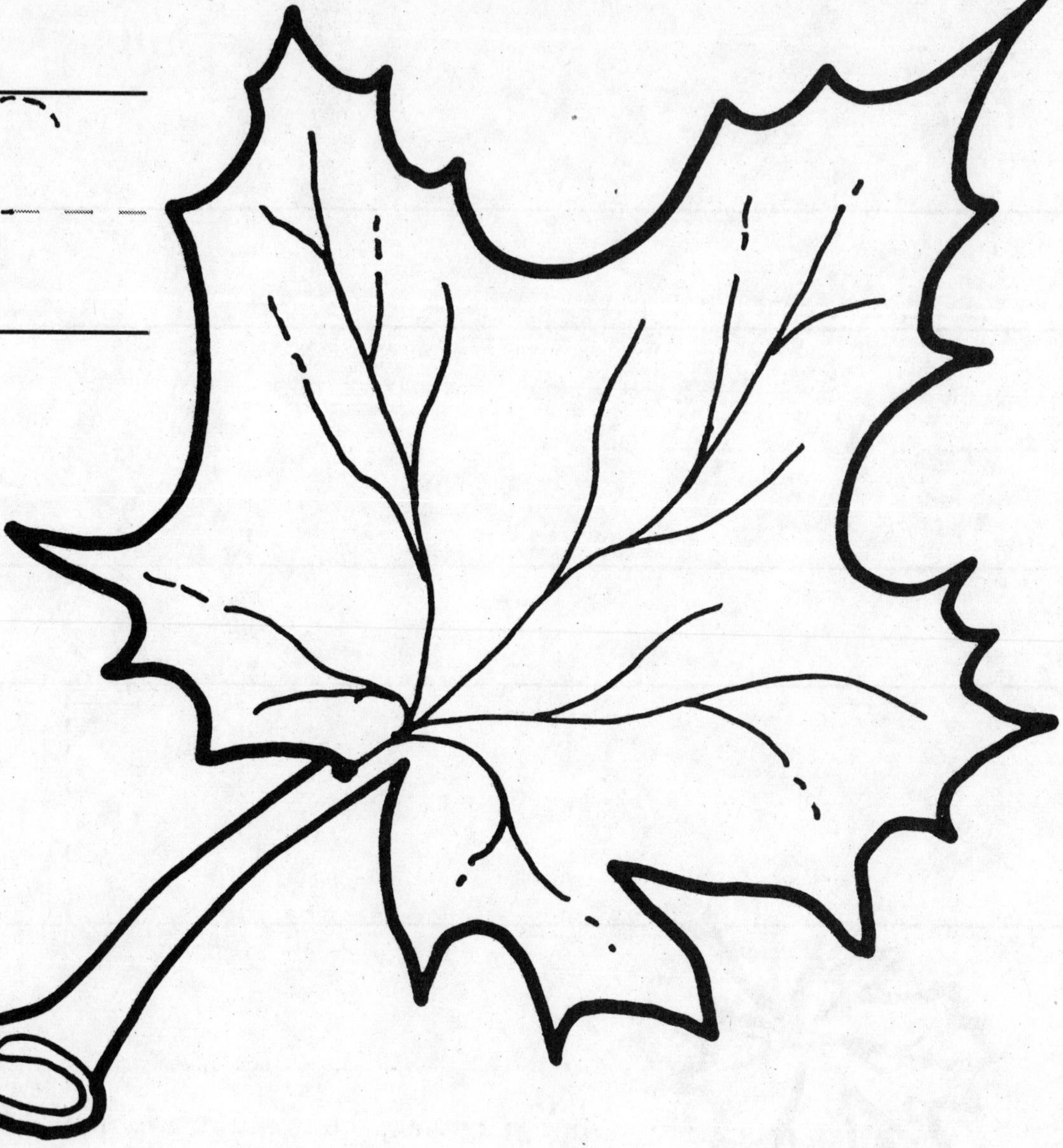

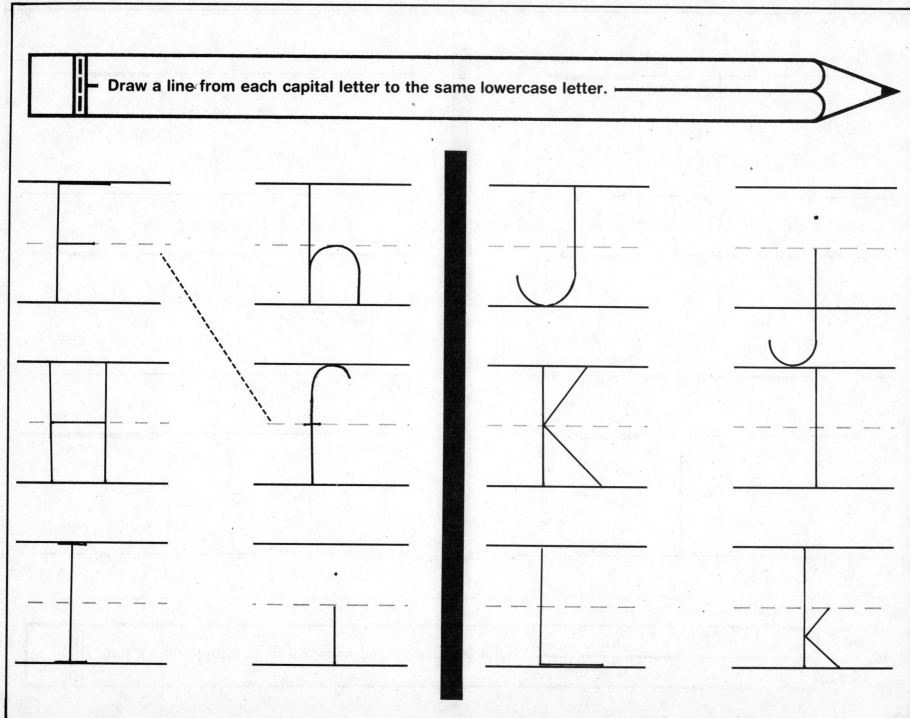

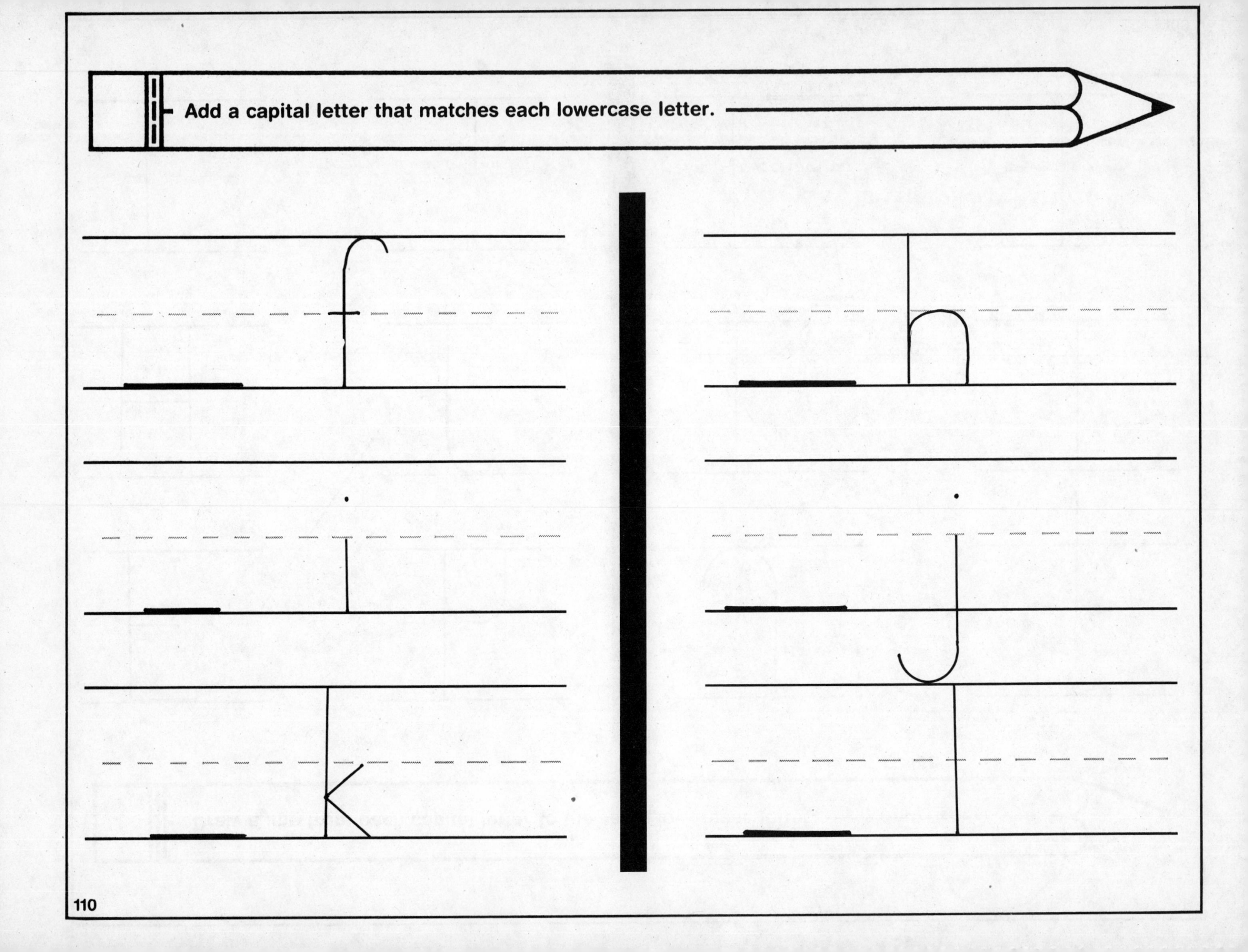

Add a capital letter that matches each lowercase letter.

110

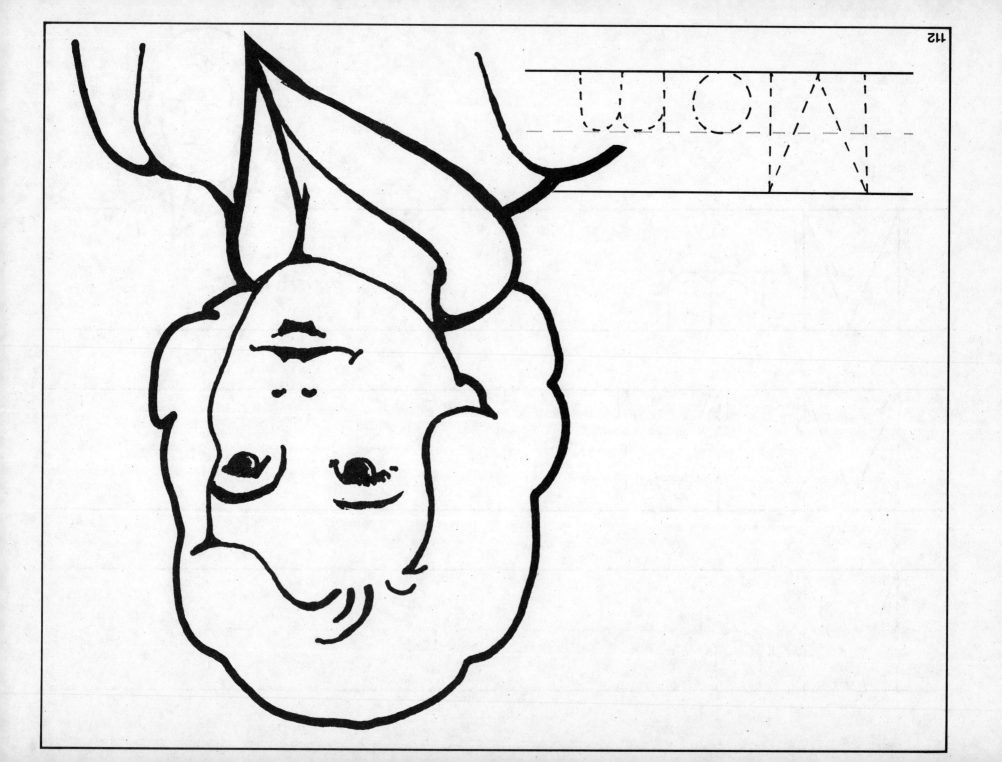

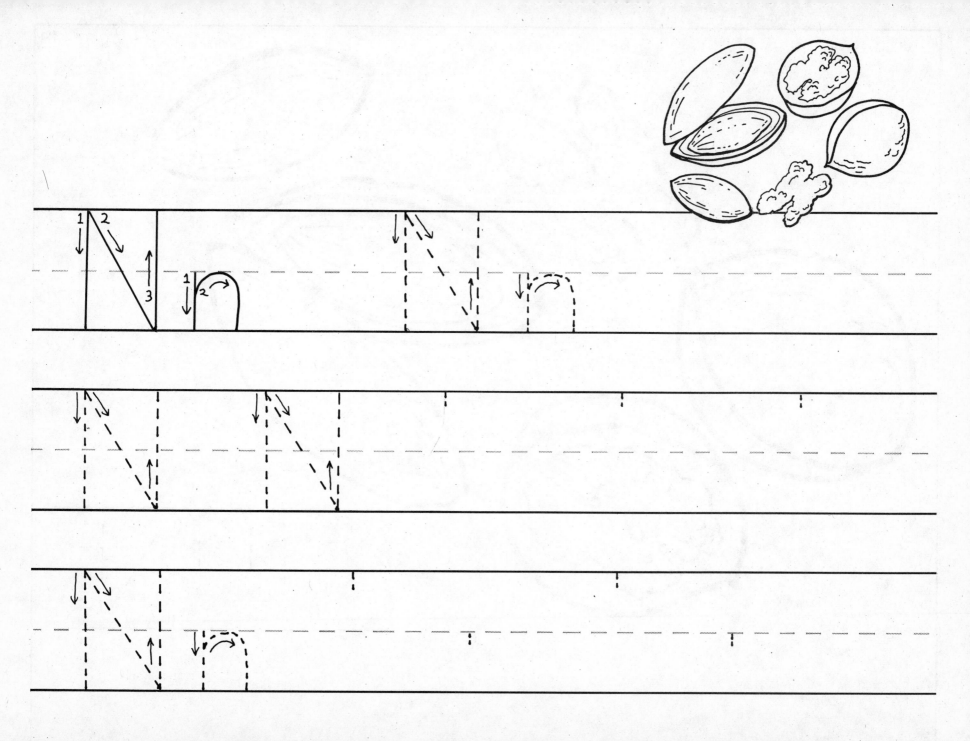

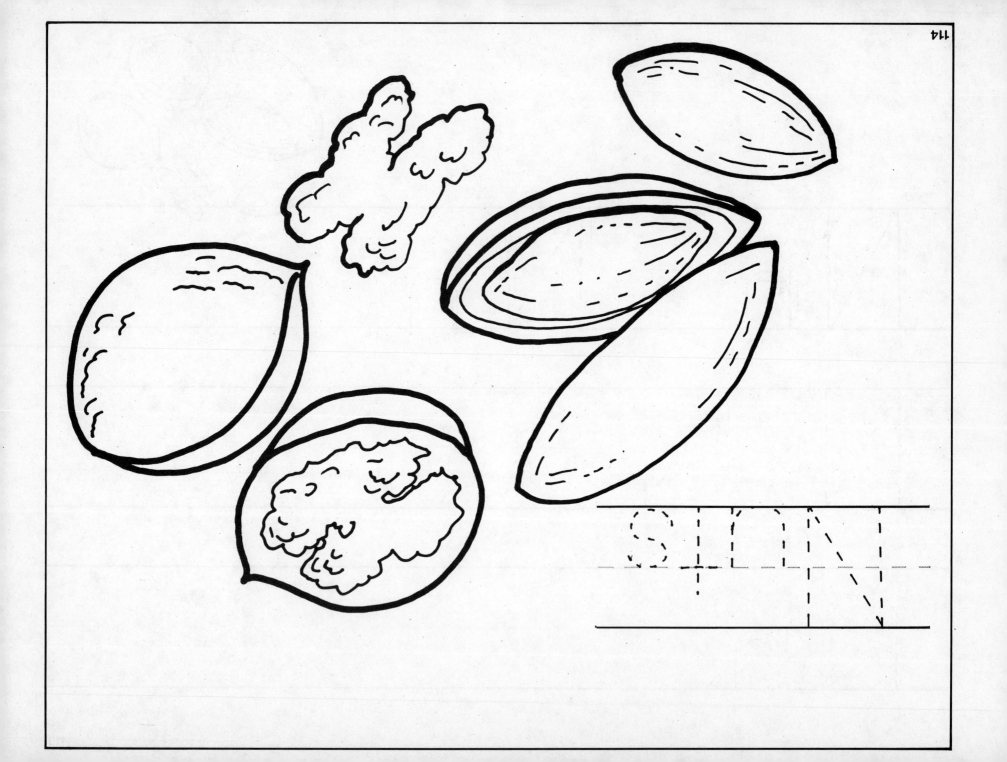

penguin

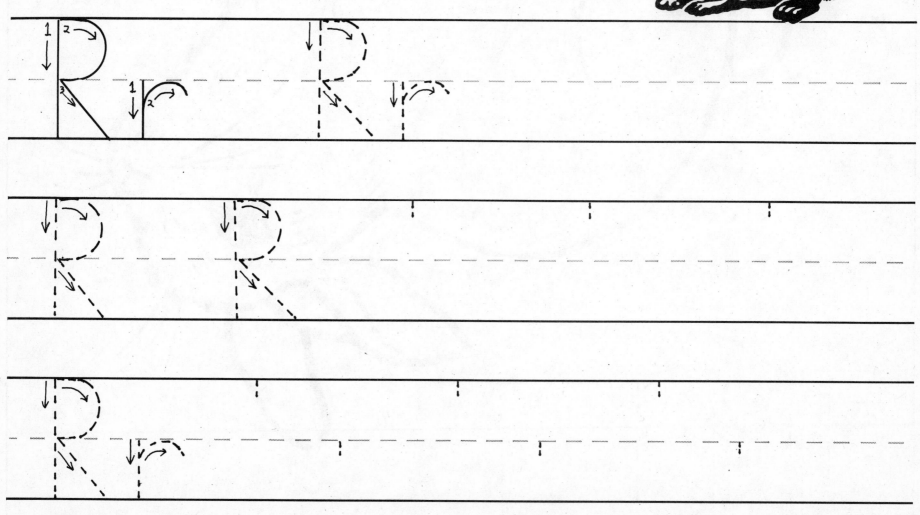

rabbit

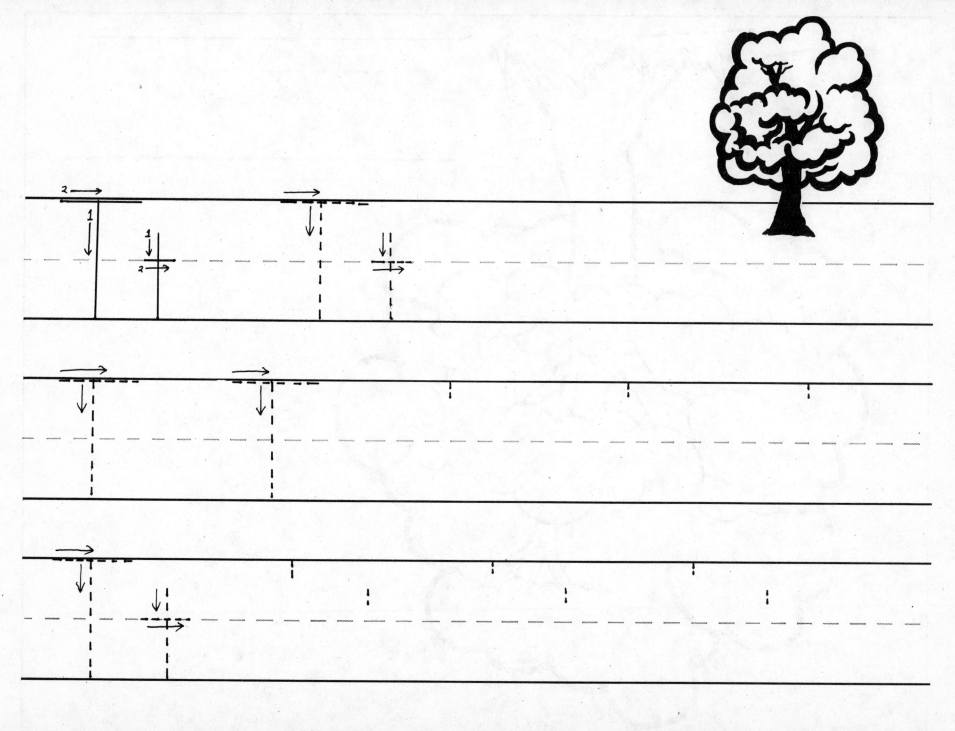

tree

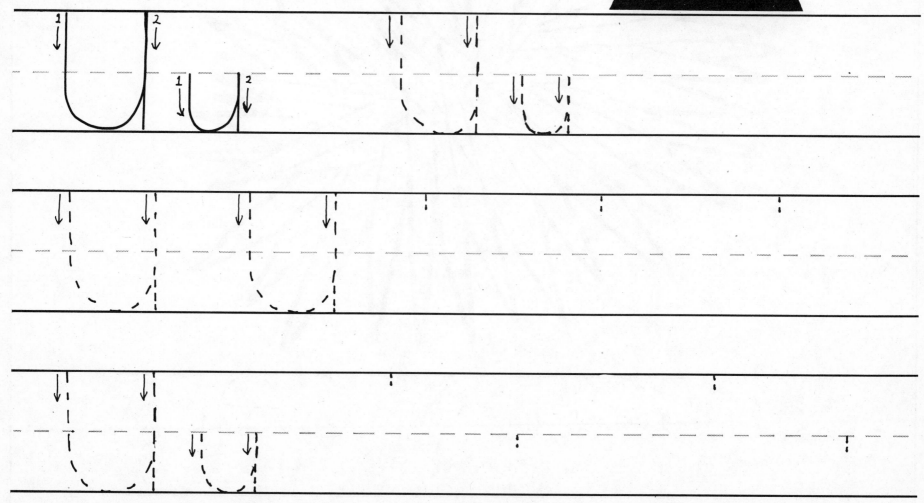

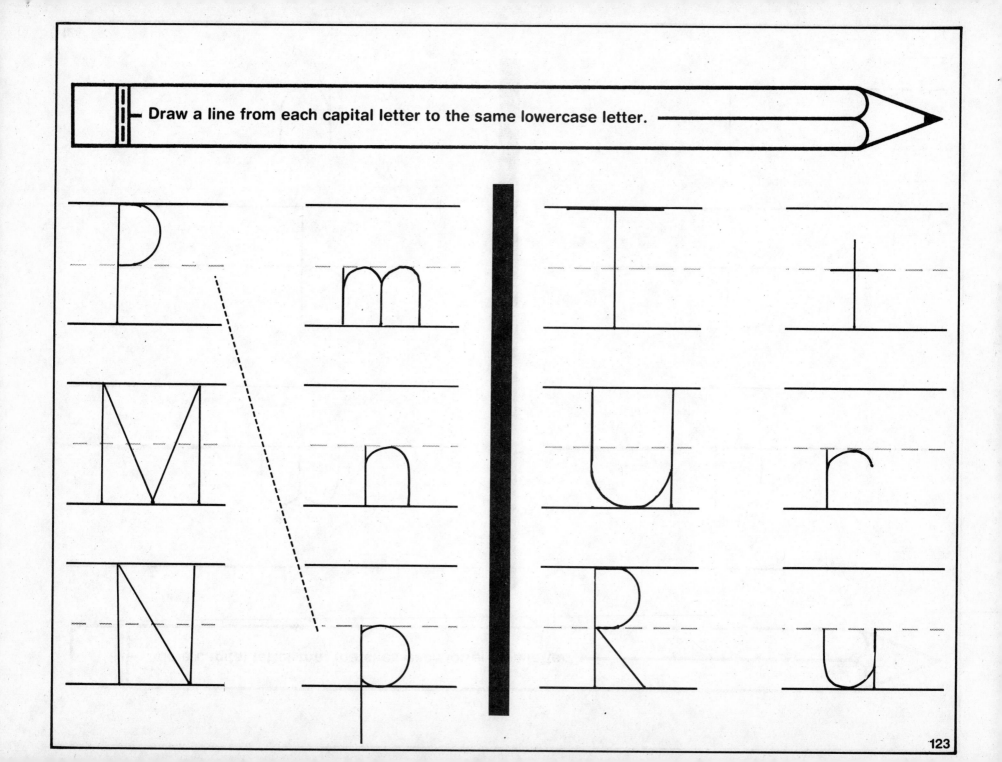

Draw a line from each capital letter to the same lowercase letter.

P

M

N

m

n

p

T

U

R

t

r

u

123

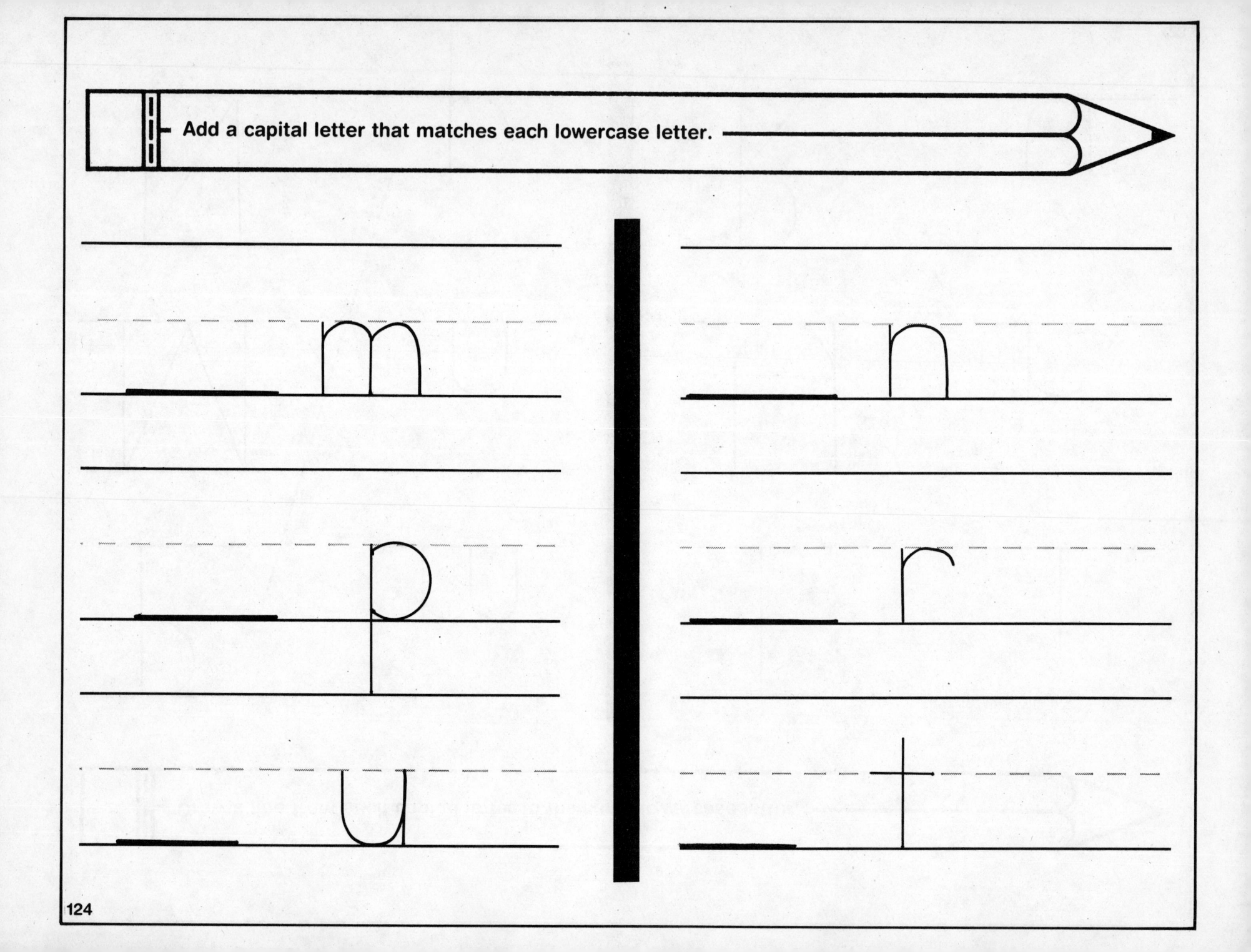

Add a capital letter that matches each lowercase letter.

m

n

p

r

u

t

124

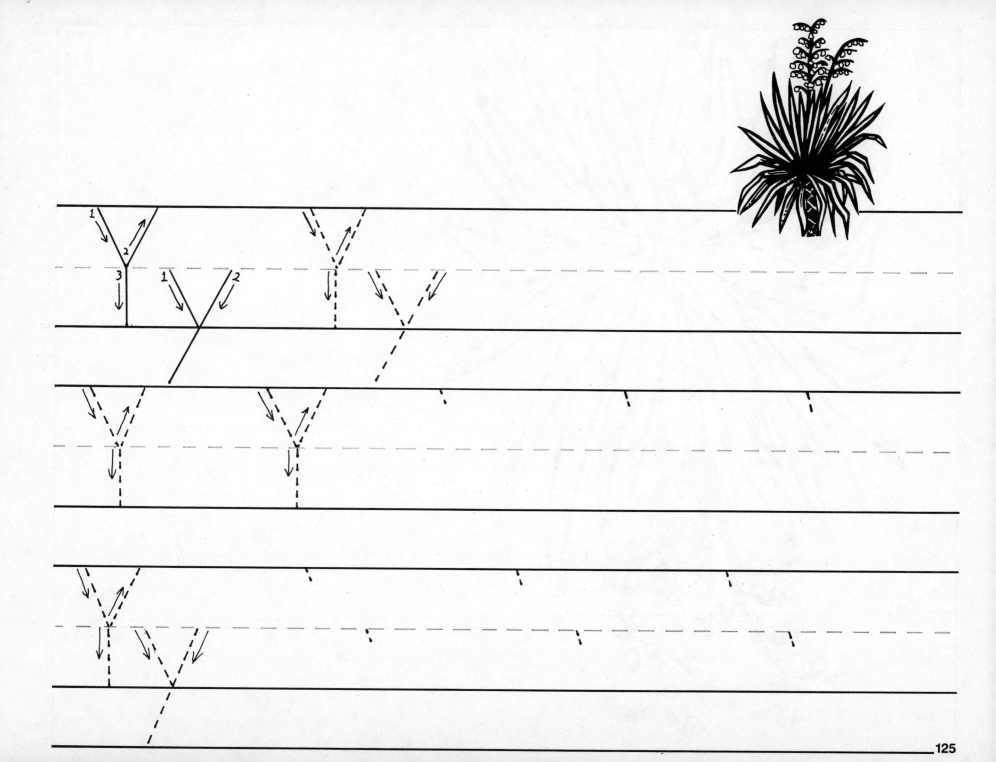

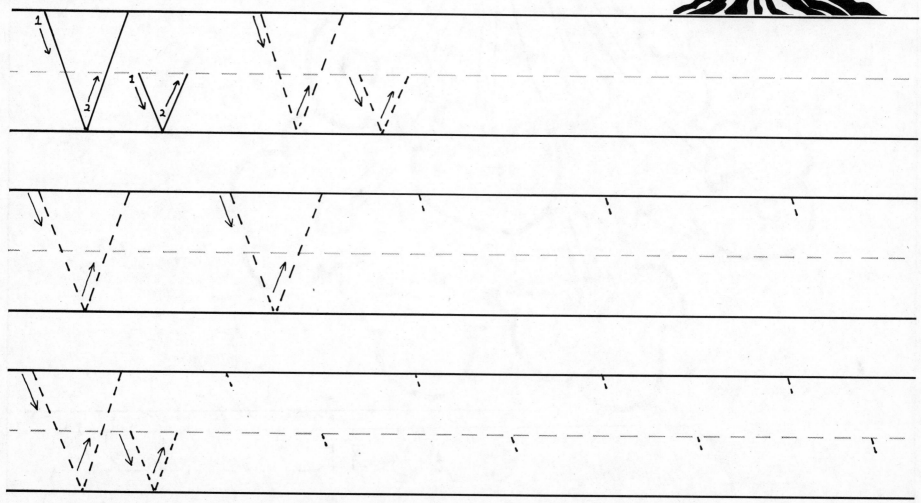

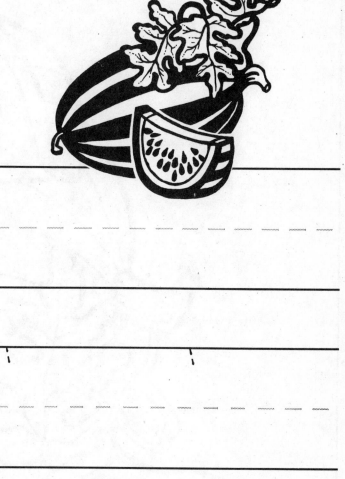

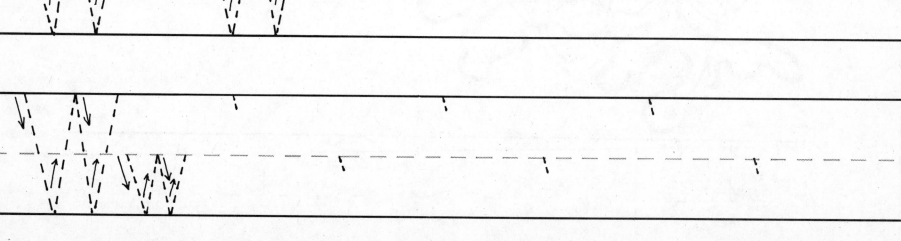

Watermelon

X as in fox

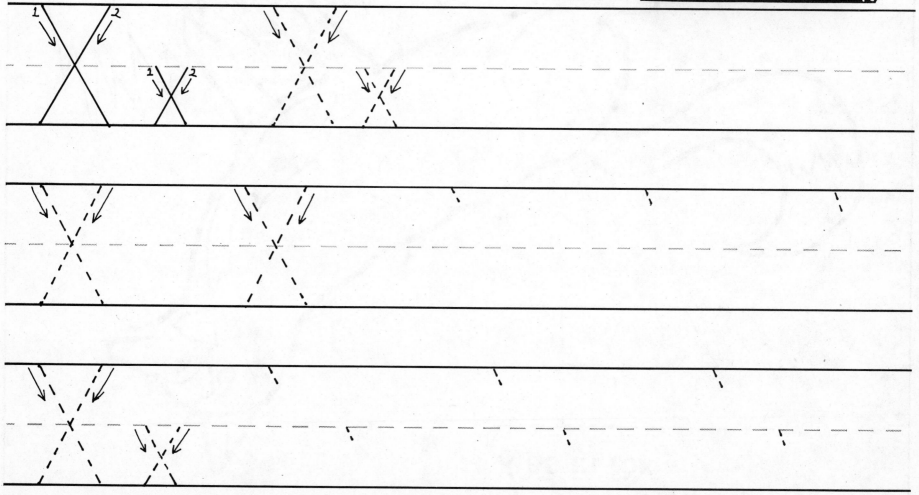

X as in fox

FOX

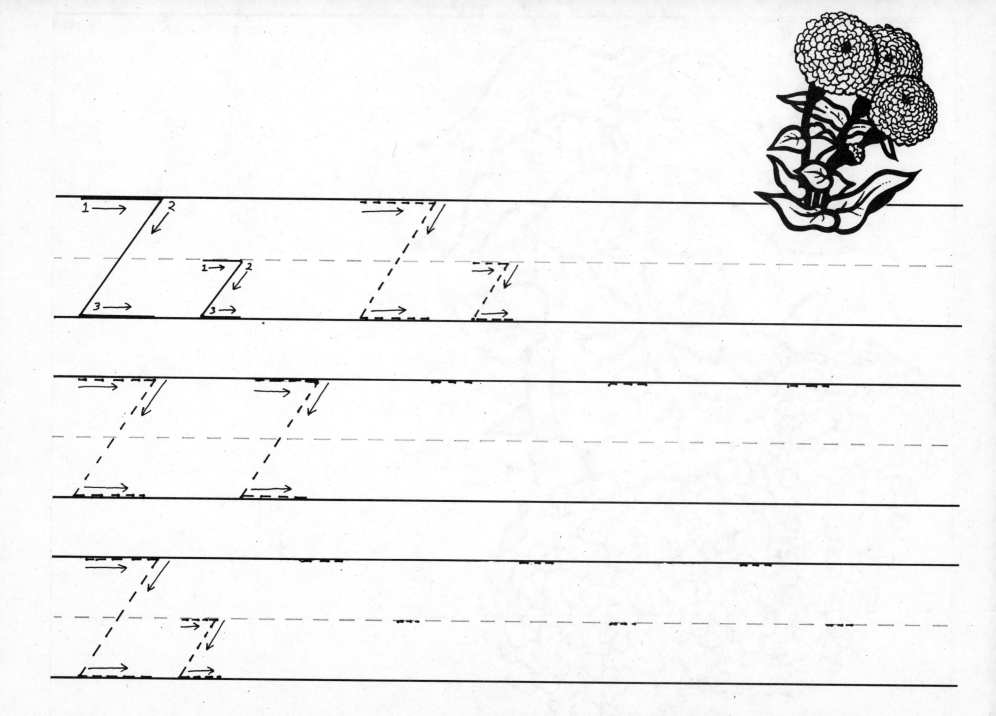

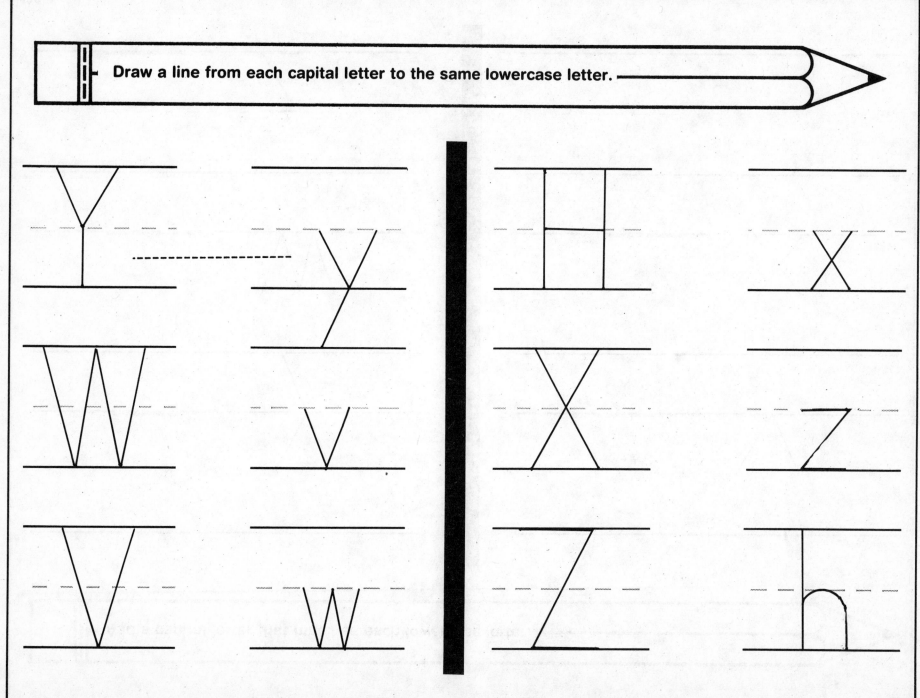

Draw a line from each capital letter to the same lowercase letter.

135

Add a capital letter that matches each lowercase letter.

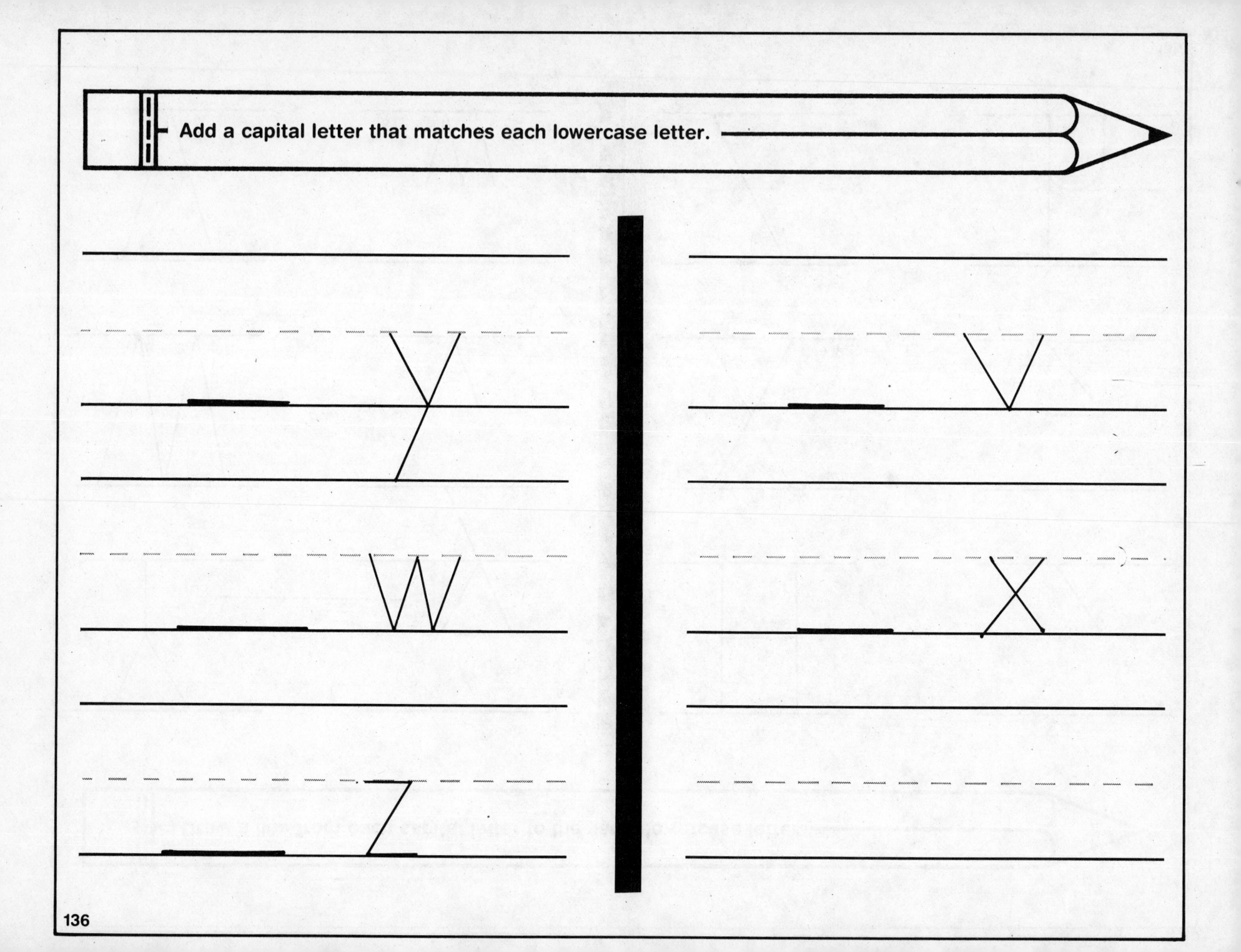

136

137

r

n

m

u

n

s

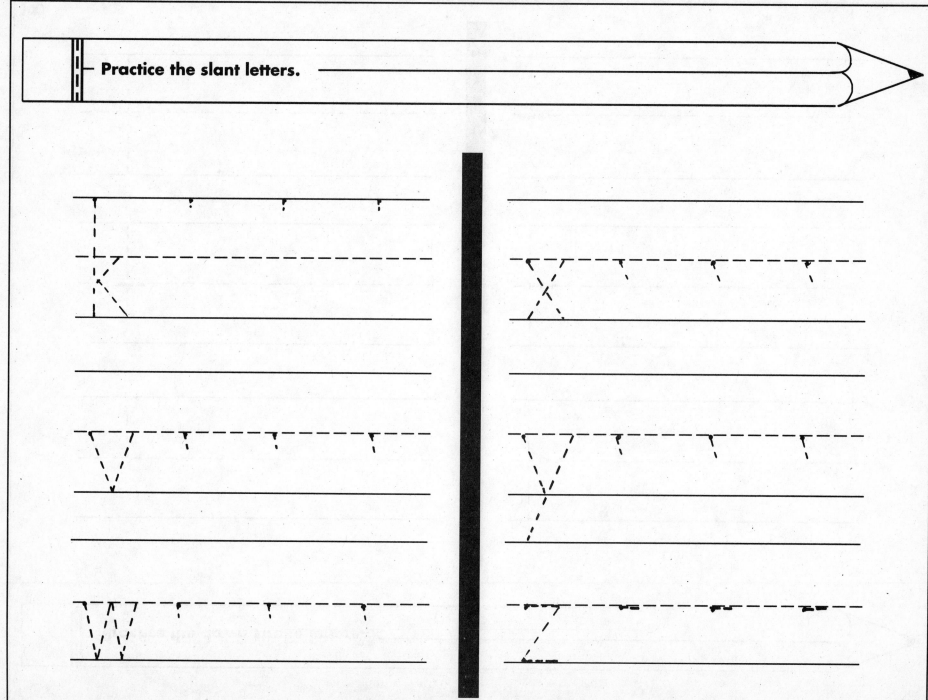

Practice the slant letters.

139

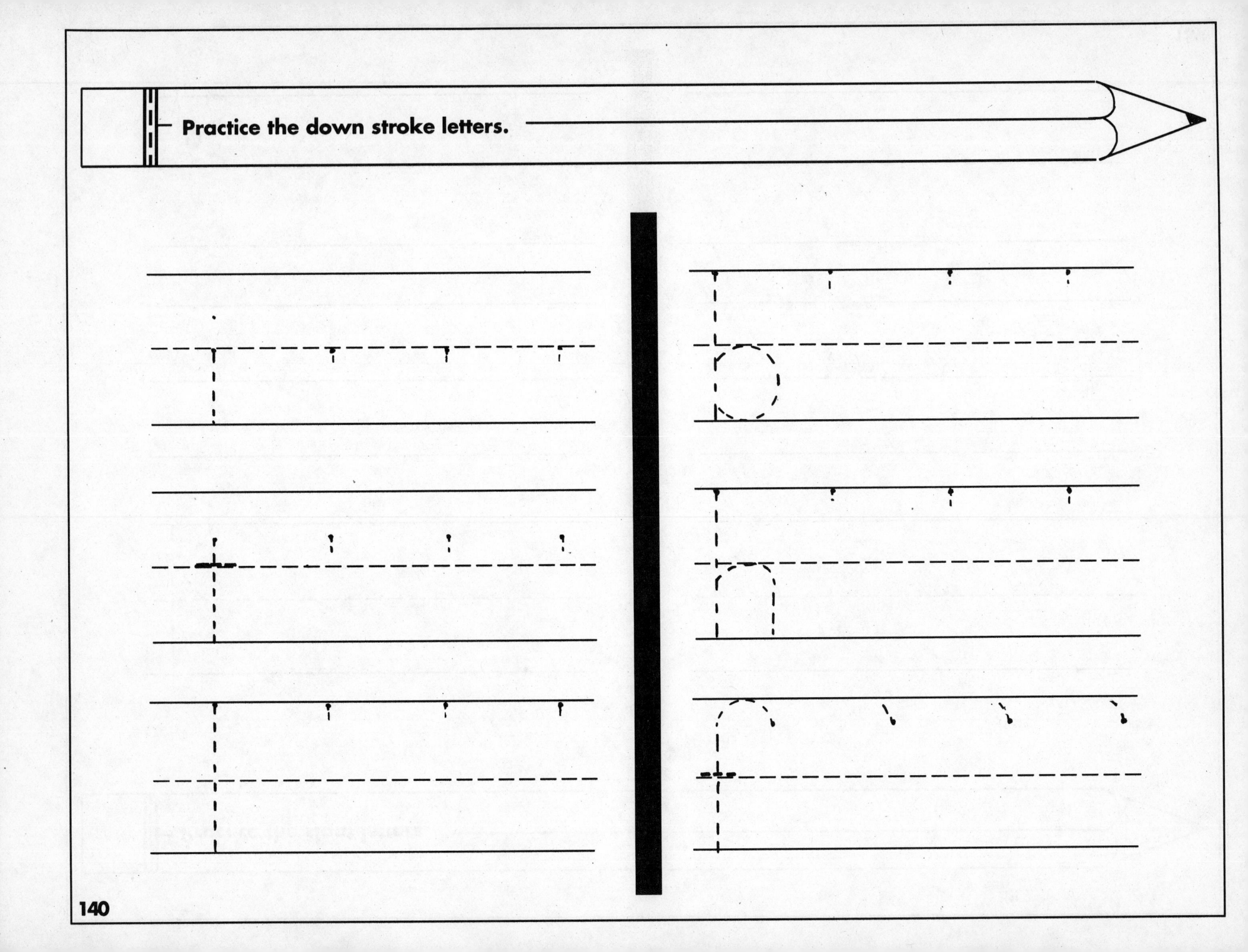

Practice the down stroke letters.

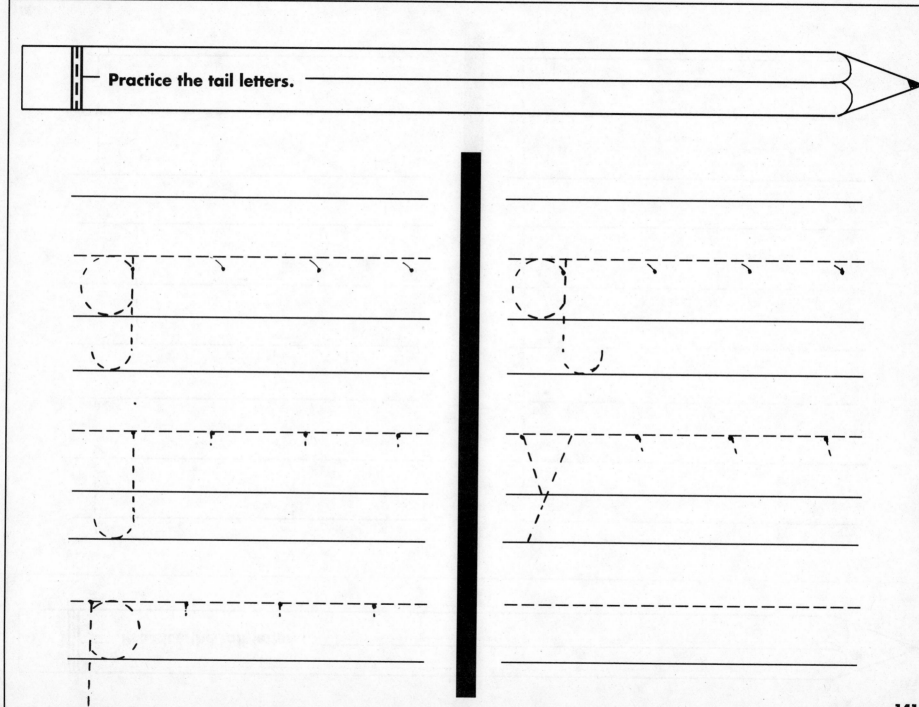

Practice the tail letters.

142